Math Thinking Motivators

by
Bob Bernstein

illustrated by Bron Smith

Cover by Vanessa Filkins

Copyright © Good Apple, Inc., 1988

ISBN No. 0-86653-431-8

Printing No. 987654321

Good Apple, Inc.
Box 299
Carthage, IL 62321-0299

Dedication

This book is dedicated to my three best friends,
Leonora, Alan
and
Robyn.

Leonora, Alan
and
Robyn

Table of Contents

Introduction

Teachers, how fortunate we are to be teachers, to be a part of this profession. How fantastic it is to be in a position where we can have a positive effect on the lives of children. How exciting it is to impart knowledge and have our students be openly receptive. How wonderful is our profession that allows for us as teachers to learn along with our students and also to learn from our students.

The excitement is in the learning, in the growing up, in the communication of ideas and thoughts and in the creativity. In short, the excitement is THE CLASS-ROOM!

The activities in this book are written with this theme in mind. The pages in the book deal with relevant subject matter. You will see unique approaches to problem solving and creativity.

As you read through the activities, keep the word *divergence* utmost in your mind. Teach divergence as opposed to strictly convergence to your children. Try leading them to various avenues when attempting solutions. Above all, encourage the positive self-image, encourage positive motivation, encourage creativity.

Wet Sponge Toss

SKILLS: Computational Skills for Basic Facts
Addition, Subtraction; Multiplication, Division
Motor Skills

On a chalkboard draw a grid similar to the one pictured below.

Select a student whose job it is to take a wet sponge (not soaking, just wet) and try to hit the chalkboard. The player must try for an area on the board that contains the numerals. Since the sponge will be wet, you should be able to determine exactly where it comes in contact with the chalkboard. If the wet print of the sponge touches the 2 and 6, the player will add the numbers and have a score of 8 points. Perhaps the sponge left wet marks on the 1, 6, and 4. In finding this sum, the player will earn 11 points. Divide the class into two teams. Select a player for each team. Each player will get three chances tossing the sponge.

When the player is ready to toss the sponge at the chalkboard, he will sit in a chair about ten feet from the board. The player sitting in the chair is to have his *back to the chalkboard*. This means that each player will have to make an over-the-shoulder toss! Good luck!

A Peek at People

SKILLS: Graphing Skills   Research
           Basic Facts   Survey
           Classification

This is an exciting activity that combines affective objectives, such as the development of a positive self-image along with positive motivation, to such mathematic concepts as the gathering and interpretation of data.

Pass out blank 3" x 5" cards to the class members. Have the students number their cards down the left-hand side, using the numerals 1 through 7. Instruct them that you will ask seven questions, and they are to record their answers in the appropriate numbered spaces.

When I grow up I want to be a Cowboy!

The seven questions to be answered are:

1. Are you a boy or a girl?

2. How old are you?

3. Which is your favorite color in the American flag—red, white, or blue?

4. Which of the following is your favorite in school—math, reading, recess, or lunch?

5. What month were you born?

6. How many sisters do you have?

7. How many brothers do you have?

A possible eighth question:

8. When I grow up I would like to become a _____.

Ask that the children not sign their names on their cards. Once all of the questions have been completed, collect all of the cards and place them in one large pile. At random, select a card from the pile and instruct those who responded positively to question 1 to please stand.

Example:
The selected card for question 1 might read:

1. "I am a girl." All of the girls in the class are to stand. Instruct the class that those who are now seated (boys) must remain in their seats throughout the remaining questions on this card.

Suppose the same card for question 2 reads:

2. "I am 11 years old." Only the girls who are 11 years old are to remain standing. The others should be seated. Remind the children who are now to sit, they are to remain seated for the remainder of the card.

"I am a girl."

After each response is read on the selected card, more children will be seated until finally only one child will be standing. Watch the excitement on the youngster's face as he first begins to realize that you are holding his card. Read four or five cards.

Math objectives may be reached by using the information supplied by the class members. You now have information that will enable you to graph the following data:

1. The number of boys and girls in class
2. The ages of the students
3. Preferred color
4. Preferred school subject
5. Birth months of the students
6. Total number of sisters
7. Total number of brothers
8. The goals that the students have in life

I am a girl.
I am 11 years old.
my favorite color is blue.

A Star Is Born

SKILLS: Gather and Interpret Data
           Graphs and Charts
           Computational Skill Facts Drill
           Ordinal and Cardinal Numbers
           Inequalities

Wouldn't it be great if each classroom contained its own huge marquee with colorful flashing lights so that all persons in the school could see the names of individual students? This would be particularly good for students who carry a poor self-image, an image of such low esteem that it is detrimental to their learning capacity. Perhaps if the shy or quiet child walked into class one day, looked up and saw his name in colorful lights, he just might think of himself as someone special who has worth and self-esteem and even as someone who **can learn**! Wouldn't it be great if teachers could get these children to actually think of themselves as winners. I can learn; I will learn; **I am a winner**!

The idea of actually having a classroom marquee is of course not probable. As teachers you can do something in its place. How about a gigantic three-foot shield similar to the one shown below?

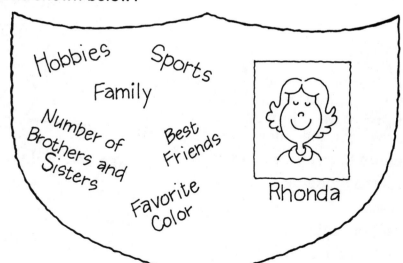

Once you have decided who the star of the day or week will be, gather relevant information about the student and either you or the student can record such information on the face of the shield. It would be extra super to have the child come to school with his picture ready to be pasted to the shield.

Criteria to determine the **star** is, of course, up to the teacher. Perhaps the teacher likes the way in which a student completes an assignment, performs a courteous act, or just wants to reward the extra effort given by the child while taking a test. There are numerous reasons as to why someone might be selected for A Star Is Born.

You also might want to consider making a smaller shield (about 18") so that each child can create his own piece. Make one so that it can be used as a tracer. Once the students decorate their own shields, a previously blank classroom wall will now become more attractive and meaningful.

This is a good time to bring in some math skills. If the shields themselves are considered to be in the realm of affective education, then the information they contain can be thought of as cognitive. The particular math skill is to gather and interpret data. Such information is now supplied by the class members for you to graph.

For example:

Our Favorite Color
Our Favorite Television Show
Our Favorite Book
The Number of Brothers and Sisters
Among Our Class Members

Time Out

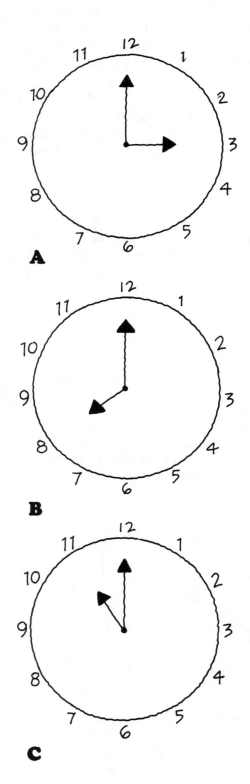

A

B

C

figure 1

SKILL: Measurement
           Time, Hour, Half Hour,
           Minute

On oaktag or poster board construct the faces of the three clocks on the left and then label them in the following way. One clock label **A**, another label **B** and label the third clock **C**. Make the face on each clock large enough so that it can be seen from almost anywhere in the room.

This activity is excellent for reviewing the concept of telling time to the hour, half hour or to five-minute intervals.

Once the clocks are constructed, set each one to the particular concept that you want to review.

In figure 1, the clocks are set to the hour. Distribute three 5 x 8 cards to each student. Each card contains one large letter, either **A**, **B**, or **C**. With reference to figure 1, ask the students to decide which of the three clocks is displaying 11:00. Remind the students not to call the answer aloud but to indicate that they know the correct response by raising the proper letter card. In this example the letter card **C** should be raised. After looking over the answer cards held by the class members, the teacher might then want to rearrange the hour and minute hand on the three clocks and once again call for a response from the students.

The same format can be applied to telling time on the half hour and at five-minute intervals.

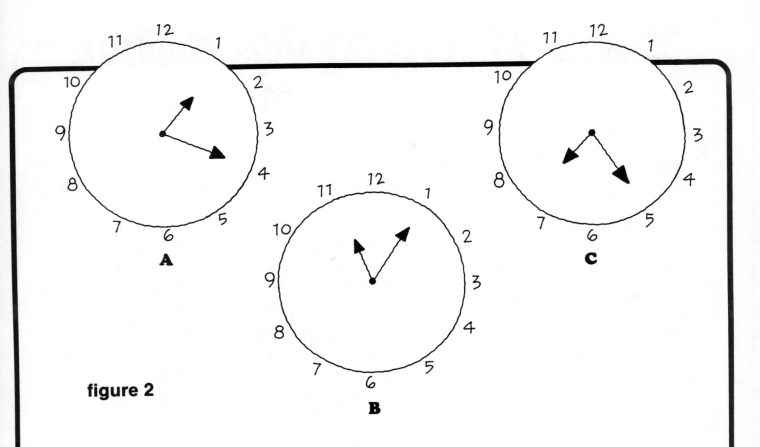

figure 2

In looking at figure 2, you might ask the children to raise the letter card that will indicate which clock is set at 11:05.

By looking at the class, the teacher can immediately see which of the students and how many of them had the correct answer. If the majority of the students had the right answer, you might want to go on to the next teaching level. If more students raised an incorrect response, you might consider reteaching the instructional objective.

Two-Minute Warning

SKILL: Basic Math Facts with Language Arts Integration

> She erased David's small label last Thursday.

Divide the class into two teams. The number of participants can be from 1 to 15 on each team. At the chalkboard, the idea is to write as many well-constructed sentences as possible within a two-minute time limit. The sentences that are written may or may not make sense. However, they must be well-constructed. Each team will be given two minutes at the chalkboard. Each team player will be assigned a number. Player one begins to write the sentence by writing the first word, player two continues the sentence and so on. A period (or question mark) may be used whenever a sentence is completed. If there is any remaining time, the players should line up at the chalkboard for a second turn. The chalk is to be passed from player to player.

In the above sample, notice that each word's initial letter is the previous word's final letter and so on.

She erased David's

In the sample, the last word is *Thursday*. If the team has any time remaining, the player at the chalkboard may begin a new sentence with a word whose initial letter must be the letter *Y*.

Once each team has completed a playing time of two minutes, both teams are ready to score. The scoring is as follows:

    a. 1 point is given for each word spelled correctly.

    b. 2 points for each vowel used (a e i o u).

    c. 3 points for all words with two or more syllables.

    d. 10 points for the mystery letter (each __).

Mystery letters (e t s o r d a b) are to be written on 3" x 5" cards. Each card is to be folded and then placed into a brown bag. Have one player from each team pick one of the cards from the bag. If the card selected is *a*, then decide how many times *a*'s are in the words used by the team and multiply that number by 10. In the sample sentence you will find six *a*'s. 6 x 10 = 60 points.

In the sample sentence the scoring would be:

a. 7 words	× 1	= 7 points	
b. 12 vowels	× 2	= 24 points	
c. 4 two-syllable words	× 3	= 12 points	
d. 6 mystery letter *a's*	× 10	= 60 points	
		103 Total score	

The team with the highest total score is declared the winner.

Who's Who?

Many of the statesmen listed below are more familiar to us than perhaps some of the others on the list. Some of these great men have a wider range of popularity among the citizens of our country. It is also true that some of these legends are carried around with us every day. They can be found in pockets, wallets and purses. It just might be that when you complete this activity, you will want to become acquainted with all of these personalities. (Some you might not wish to carry on your person.) The historic legends that you previously did not know just might turn out to be the very characters you would now enjoy learning about.

Can you match the denominations of money on the left with the statesmen on the right?

a.	$1	Hamilton	_____
b.	$2	Franklin	_____
c.	$5	McKinley	_____
d.	$10	Grant	_____
e.	$20	Jefferson	_____
f.	$50	Chase	_____
g.	$100	Washington	a
h.	$500	Wilson	_____
i.	$1000	Jackson	_____
j.	$5000	Madison	_____
k.	$10,000	Lincoln	_____
* l.	$100,000	Cleveland	_____

*These bills are no longer in circulation.

10

President Andrew Jackson has his picture on the twenty dollar bill. Using some of the currency denominations listed, how many different ways can you create a cash value equal to this amount?

Example:

Jackson = 2 Hamiltons

or

1 Hamilton + 10 Washingtons

or

10 Jeffersons

Problem A: Record the cash values equal to the Federal Reserve Note bearing the picture of President Ulysses S. Grant.

Problem B: You will find the picture of Benjamin Franklin on the $100 bill. You might be interested to know that there are 293 ways of creating this amount using these denominations of currency. List all of the different ways you can find.

The Price Must Be Right

SKILLS: Inequalities
Money
Estimation
Rounding off Numbers
Reading Numbers
Multiples

If you leaf through the pages of various magazines and cut out pictures of advertised products (especially those items that would hold the most interest for your students), you will have the basic ingredients for a highly motivational activity that deals with such math concepts as estimation, rounding off numbers, and reading and writing large numbers. Paste the cutout pictures on sheets of 8″ x 10″ oaktag or poster board. The pictures that would probably generate the most interest might be those of television sets, video recorders, stereos, bicycles, toys and clothing. You will need twelve to eighteen pictures for this activity. Once you have decided to use a picture, paste it on one side of the oaktag. On the other side of the oaktag, record the retail price of the item. Write this amount to the nearest dollar, tens of dollars or hundreds of dollars.

Example: **figure 1**

front

back

Choose someone from the class to begin play. Inform this person that his job is to discover the correct price of the item shown on the oaktag. The player is to make guesses and round them off to the nearest tens of dollars. To accomplish this, players are given sixty seconds. Once the player gives the initial estimate, the teacher responds with an appropriate "Higher" or "Lower." If the correct price is uncovered within the allowable time frame, any remaining seconds will dictate just how much time the player has available to try for a second and perhaps more valuable prize (an automobile). The player would be allowed the remaining seconds to attempt to discover the cost of the automobile to the nearest hundreds of dollars.

This example refers to figure 1. The player will see only the picture of a television set. The picture is held by the teacher so that the class (not the player) can see the retail cost of the item. For this first prize, estimates should be rounded off to the closest tens of dollars. Follow this interaction (price of the TV set is $620):

Player's initial guess for the cost of the TV set: $450
Teacher's response: higher
Player: $550
Teacher: higher
Player: $650
Teacher: lower
Player: $600
Teacher: higher
Player: $610
Teacher: higher
Player: $620
Teacher: Correct, the prize is yours.

The teacher should now determine the amount of time the player has remaining from the original sixty seconds and allow this amount of time for a similar interaction with regard to the new prize and its cost.

Wagons or 'Vettes

SKILLS: Graphing Skills   Basic Facts   Classification
         Research   Survey

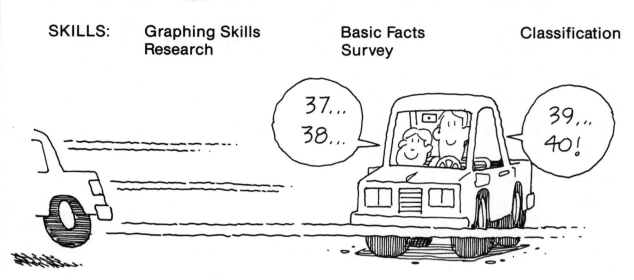

For many students the idea of gathering and interpreting data has proven to be a most interesting learning experience. Throughout the course of our daily activities, many interesting happenings pass us by (literally). For example, you may be waiting at an intersection for a bus and a large number of automobiles might pass by. Perhaps the following questions may have occurred to you.

1. What is the percentage of station wagons among all these automobiles?

2. Which is more popular, the two-door or four-door car?

3. Are there more automobiles passing this intersection that have only the driver or are there more cars passing with the driver and one or more passengers?

4. If your favorite automobile is the Corvette, what is the percentage of Corvettes to the total number of automobiles passing this intersection?

5. What is the percentage of foreign-made cars to U.S.-made automobiles?

To formulate your conclusions, you might want to create a graph on the topic of your choice, gathering information perhaps three or four times a week at various locations and at different time periods throughout the day.

The following is the result of a three-week survey regarding the question of the percentage of station wagons to the total number of automobiles.

Date	Location	Time	Station Wagons	Total Cars	Percentage
2/4	2nd & Pine	8:30 a.m.	15	100	
2/5	Bridge	8:47 a.m.	9	100	
2/6	Bridge	10:30 a.m.	10	100	
2/11	Oak Penrose	3:15 p.m.	11	100	
2/12	17th Race	3:30 p.m.	8	100	
2/13	Bridge	11:47 a.m.	11	100	
2/19	Broad-East	9:00 a.m.	18	100	
2/20	Bridge	5:00 p.m.	16	100	
2/21	Turnpike	8:43 a.m.	12	100	
			110	900	

The percentage of station wagons to automobiles is 12%.

Repeat this procedure four weeks from now and see if the results are the same.

Brainteaser I

SKILLS: Problem-Solving Skills
Measurement
Gather and Interpret Data

Shannon is one of the greatest cookie bakers of all time. Aside from such obvious ingredients as flour, butter and eggs, her true secret ingredient is water. Shannon says that her cookies must have exactly four ounces of water. To hold the water, she uses a jar that will contain, when full, exactly five ounces and a jar that, when it is full, will contain exactly three ounces. There are absolutely no markings on either jar other than their five-ounce and three-ounce labels. As stated earlier, Shannon wants to have exactly four ounces of water to support her baking needs.

Please know that Shannon has access to all the water she may need by using the tap in the kitchen sink. Also know that there are no other jars available to her. The problem is, therefore, with all of this water available and with only a five-ounce and three-ounce jar, how can Shannon be sure that she will have exactly **four ounces of water**?

In thinking this problem through, there are different ways to solve it.

SOLUTION:
1. Fill three-ounce jar with water.
2. Pour this into five-ounce jar.
3. Fill three-ounce jar again.
4. Pour this water into five-ounce jar. There should be one ounce left in the three-ounce jar and the five-ounce jar is now full.
5. Pour out all water in the five-ounce jar.
6. Pour the one ounce left in the three-ounce jar into the five-ounce jar.
7. Fill the three-ounce jar again and pour the contents into the five-ounce jar. The jar should contain four ounces of water.

Brainteaser II

SKILLS: Problem-Solving Skills
            Measurement
            Gather and Interpret Data

Suppose there were a stack of paper plates in front of you similar to that in figure A. Perhaps the stack of plates is about twenty inches high. How could you determine the number of plates in this stack? Of course you can count each individual plate. But, is there some other way (other than guessing) that you could arrive at a fairly accurate answer? There are various approaches in trying to arrive at an answer. One might be the idea of halving.

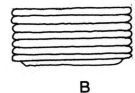

figure A

SOLUTION:
1. From the original stack, make two stacks that seem to be half and half.

| A | = | B | + | B |

2. Repeat this procedure (break down one of the B piles into halves or B = C + C), until you have a stack of about 10 plates.
3. Once your stack has about 10 plates, the procedure is reversed. Two stacks of 10 plates each will equal 20 plates. The 20-plate stack and its matching half will equal 40 plates and so on until you reach stack B plus B which together will give you the number of plates in stack A.

Brainteaser III

A number that can be read forward and backward and still remain the same number has a special name. It is called a palindrome. 515, 1331, 64146 and 8372738 are all examples of palindromic numbers. An example of non-palindromic numbers would be 514, 1330, 64145, and 8374259. Palindromic numbers appear many times each day in our daily lives. All you have to do is refer to the display on a digital clock. The question that now arises is, "How many palindromic numbers will be displayed on a digital clock throughout the entire day?"

Examples of such palindromes are 2:42, 7:57, and 10:01. Your job, should you choose to accept it, is to find the total number of these particular palindromes.

If you enjoyed this asssignment, your next job is to determine the exact number of palindromes displayed on a military clock*.

The answers are listed on the next page.

*On this military clock, the first 9 hours are displayed with **no 0** to the left of the hour.
    Examples: 1:42, 7:23

Regular Digital Clock

A.
1:01	2:02	3:03	4:04	5:05	6:06	7:07	8:08	9:09
1:11	2:12	3:13	4:14	5:15	6:16	7:17	8:18	9:19
1:21	2:22	3:23	4:24	5:25	6:26	7:27	8:28	9:29
1:31	2:32	3:33	4:34	5:35	6:36	7:37	8:38	9:39
1:41	2:42	3:43	4:44	5:45	6:46	7:47	8:48	9:49
1:51	2:52	3:53	4:54	5:55	6:56	7:57	8:58	9:59

There are 6 palindromes in each column.
There are 9 columns, for a total of 54 palindromes; however, don't forget

10:01
11:11
12:21 for a total of 57 palindromes.

The question was what was the total number of palindromes in a day.

Answer: 57 x 2 = <u>114</u> palindromic numbers displayed on a
digital clock throughout a 24-hour day.

B. The answer to the number of palindromes displayed on a military clock
throughout the day is <u>61</u>, the 54 listed above

plus   13:31
14:41
15:51
20:02
21:12
22:22
23:32

Brainteaser IV

Imagine yourself being in a very dark room with all the shades drawn and all the lights turned off. As your eyes begin to adjust to the situation, you start to see some light and it seems to be coming from the digital clock. Perhaps you begin to notice some changes in the intensity of the light as the digits change from one minute to another. At some times the light becomes brighter and at other times its intensity lessens. Each moment of the day has its own specific formation with a specific number of segments.

has 3 segments   has 6 segments

The reference line below will help you solve problems relating to the digital clock.

6   2   5   5   4   5   6   3   7   6

number of segments

---

1. The problem is, at what time will the display on the digital clock be at its brightest? How many segments will be displayed?
2. At what time will the digital clock display show the least intensity? How many segments will be displayed?
3. Can you find the next brightest display time?

ANSWERS:

1. 10:08 = 21 segments

2. 1:11 = 6 segments

3. 8:08 = 20 segments

   or

   10:58 = 20 segments

20

Did You See That?

SKILLS: Estimation
Patterning
Computational Skills
Averaging

On a card measuring 8" x 10", repro-
duce the illustration as shown in figure
A.

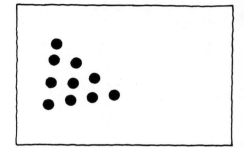

figure A

Inform the class that you will be
showing them a card that contains
dots. Tell class members that they will
see the card for three seconds. After
this they must decide on the number
of dots they think they saw. The clue
words and the most important words
for this activity are **what you think you
saw**! At the very beginning of this
activity, stress that the students do
their own thinking. If someone looks
at figure A and thinks that he saw 18
dots and you think you saw something
different, you must not be swayed from
your original decision. Stick with the
number of dots that you thought you
initally saw. The cards in figures A and
B are purposely arranged in a pattern
form.

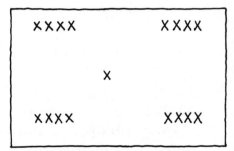

figure B

Once the teacher or leader shows the card for the three-second limit, the next step is to ask all students how many objects they thought they saw on the given card. At the chalkboard, list all of the student responses in a column, addition format.

Example:

Student responses to figure A

```
10
12
 9
12
14
12
10
 8
10
 8
 9
 8
 9
10
10
───
151
```

Once you determine the sum of all the responses, divide that total by the number of students who participated. In this example, 15 ⟌151, the average response is 10. On the lower right corner of each card is the exact answer as to the number of objects on the face of the card. Before disclosing this information to the students, inform them that if an answer (average number) is in the teens, we will use a range of plus or minus 1. This is to say that the range of the answer in the above example at 10 with a plus or minus 1 means that we expect the answer to fall in the range of 9, 10 or 11.

If when calculating the average response an answer is in the twenties, the range should be plus or minus 2. As an example, an average response of 28 would provide a range of 26, 27, 28, 29, and 30. Therefore if the exact answer on a card is 26 and the combined average turned out to be 28, then the combined average would be in the accepted range.

Combined averages in the forties would have a range of plus or minus 4. With combined averages in the fifties, the range would be plus or minus 5, etc.

Suggestions for additional 8" x 10" cards might be:

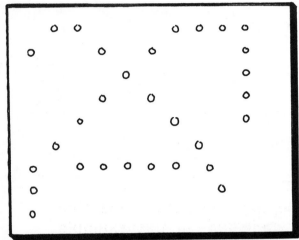

figure C

K D B Q B Z F J B D R
L D S F S D N M L O
Z G H N S C D M Y A L
F O I J P A G V B A
M N G H B D N O J Q Z
B D Z Q R N B C J Z G L
M A B G R Z B D G V B
R N B C V L Y T M Z T
V Z T G H B R N O S

figure D

Bobby Joe Brenda Butch
Brad Larry Bonnie Jeremy
Betty Eric Jacquie Jannelle Linda
Annette Tom Tamara Ryan
Valerie Seth Josh Shannon

(Names of your students)

figure E

Baltimore Concord Memphis
New York Dover Tulsa Troy
El Paso Reno Miami
Boston Oakland
Santa Fe Detroit
Trenton Philadelphia
Portland Seattle Kennewick
Chehalis

figure F

Liquid Measurement Dry!

SKILL: Liquid Measurement
            Cups, Pints, Quarts,
            Half-Gallons, Gallons

Liquid Measurement Dry is a great way to learn all about liquid measurement facts and **never get wet!** This is a game that will require construction of the following pieces:

4 gameboards similar to this one:

front

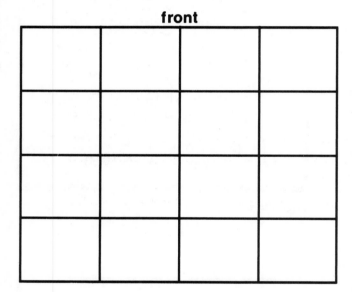

The measurement for each board is 16" x 16".

back

full gallon

1 pint

16 pieces
4" x 8"

1 cup

20 pieces
4" x 4"

24

1 quart

Half-gallon

12 pieces,
4″ x 16″

8 pieces,
8″ x 16″

This activity would be much more attractive as well as more effective if all the cups were in red, all the pints in yellow, all the quarts in light blue, all the half-gallons in orange and all the full gallons in white.

An additional required material is at least 16 playing cards (4″ x 4″) illustrated below.

| Ask for 1 cup. | You may have 1 cup. | Ask for 2 cups. | Ask for 1 cup. |

| Sorry! No cups for you. | You may have 1 cup. | You may have 2 cups. | Ask for 1 cup. |

| You may have 2 cups. | Ask for 2 cups. | 1 quart for you. | 1 pint for you. |

| Change seats with the other team! | 1 cup for you. | Please return 1 cup. | Ask for 1 cup. |

Once all of the pieces are ready, play may begin. This game is for two teams. Each team may consist of one to four players. Each team will have before them two gameboards (16"x16" full gallons). The winning team is the first team to completely fill both gameboards. Someone should be designated to act as a referee. When first introducing the game to students, it might be best if the teacher assumes the role of the referee.

The referee starts the action by informing the players that the object of the game is to completely fill both gallon mats by using the available cups, pints, quarts, and half-gallons. A main rule guiding the activity is that at no time can a player have two pieces of the same denomination on his/her mat.

Players will be given the dry liquid measurement pieces according to each player's draw of the playing cards. The playing cards are to be shuffled and left in a pile facedown.

Follow this action:
Player A draws a playing card and suppose it reads, "You may have 1 cup." The referee would give one (red) cup to player A. The player would then place the (red) cup onto his/her gallon mat. Refer to figure 1.

figure 1

1 cup

Player A's mat

Remember... no player may have two pieces of the same kind on a mat!

Player B then takes a turn by drawing a playing card. Again, according to the card, the referee will give player B the prescribed part or parts indicated on the playing card. Perhaps player B's card read, "Ask for 2 cups." The referee would then give the player 2 (red) cups. B would place them on his/her mat.

At this point, the referee would remind all of the players about the rule that states, "No player may have two pieces of the same kind on a mat." Therefore player B will have to return 2 (red) cups to the referee and will in return receive 1 (yellow) pint.

Examine figures 2 and 3.

figure 2

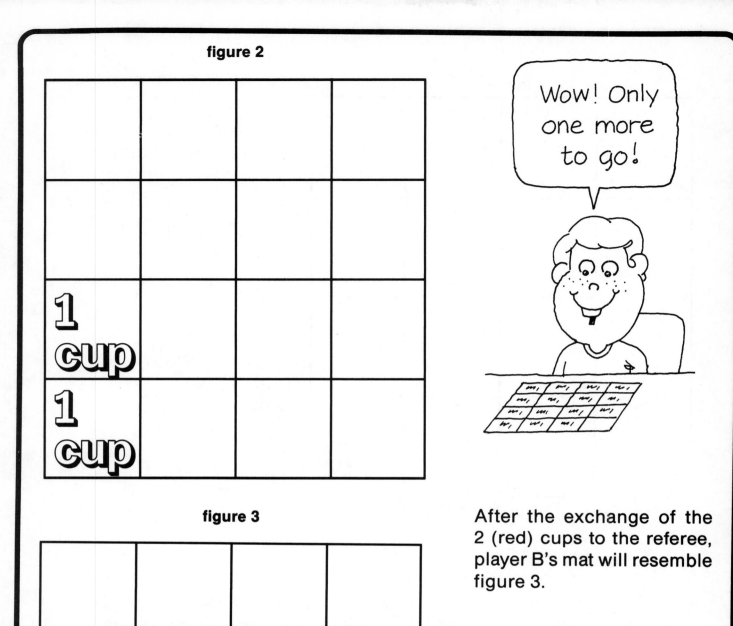

1 cup
1 cup

Wow! Only one more to go!

figure 3

1 pint

After the exchange of the 2 (red) cups to the referee, player B's mat will resemble figure 3.

Play continues in this manner until one team has filled both gallon mats. The team doing this first is the winning team.

The back and forth trading of 2 (yellow) pints for 1 (light blue) quart leads to a better understanding of liquid measurement.

For example:
1 (orange) half-gallon = 2 (light blue) quarts
     or = 4 (yellow) pints
     or = 8 (red) cups
     or = 1 (light blue) quart and 2 (yellow) pints

Try some of these problems:

Rename 3 (yellow) pints
   example = 6 (red) cups
        = 1 (light blue) quart and 1 (yellow) pint
        = 1 (light blue) quart and 2 (red) cups

Rename:
 1 quart   1 gallon   12 cups

Secret Letter

SKILLS: Computational Skills
          Basic Addition Facts to 63
          Exponents/Binary System
          Mental Math

If you have ever wondered whether or not you have mental powers, the answer is probably you do. Follow the rules for this activity and you will be able to mentally name, and then call aloud, a letter that someone else has secretly chosen. Have someone select a letter from the alphabet. The person is to keep the letter *secret!* Ask the person to concentrate on that particular letter in the letter chart and then tell you *all* of the colors that the selected letter appears in. After noting all of the colors in your mind, you must now look to the lower left corner of the letter chart and you will see five main colors. These are the colors found in the letters P, A, B, H, and D. What you must now mentally do is give the letters, along with their colors, the following values:

P = red = 16,   A = white = 1,   B = yellow = 2,   H = blue = 8, and
D = green = 4.

Now to determine the so called "secret letter," you must remember all of the colors that the person called out, convert the colors to numerals and reach their sum total.

Example: Suppose someone said, "My letter is found in red, green and white." With this information you can discover the *secret letter*. You must now remember that red = 16, green = 4, and white = 1. (16 + 4 + 1 = 21) Since there are 26 letters in the alphabet, all you need to know is which of the letters is the 21st. (The answer of secret letter is U.)

Additional examples:

Blue, yellow, white = 8 + 2 + 1 = 11 (the letter K)

Green, yellow = 4 + 2 = 6 (the letter F)

Red, yellow, white =

Red, blue, green, white =

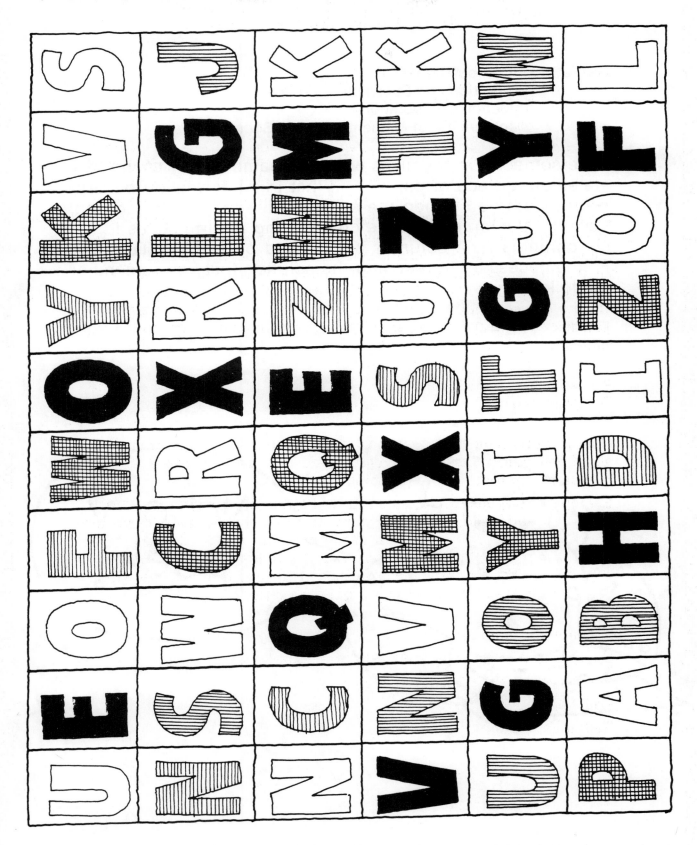

A State of Mind

SKILLS: Computational Skills
Addition and Subtraction Facts to 63
Mental Computation
Integration of Mathematics with Social Studies

Have someone in the class write the name of any of the fifty states on a piece of paper. Ask that this information be kept secret from you. When the selection is made and recorded, have the person look at the chart listing all fifty states in the six columns. The columns are headed by A, B, C, D, E and F. It is necessary in reaching the solution that you remember the following:

F = 1   E = 2   D = 4   C = 8   B = 16   A = 32

For example: When the choice is made and recorded, have the student indicate to you all of the columns that the particular state can be found. Perhaps the response is, "Columns B, E and F." You must then substitute the numerical value for each letter. In this case, B, E and F are equal to 16 + 2 +1 for a sum of 19. Take the sum and refer it to the fifty-state decoder. You will see that the nineteenth state listed in alphabetical order is Maine. Another example: Suppose the secret selection is found in columns A, D and E. You must know that A = 32, D = 4 and E = 2 for a sum of 38. The thirty-eighth state listed in alphabetical order in the fifty-state decoder is Pennsylvania.

STATE CHART

A
New York
North Carolina
North Dakota
Ohio
Oklahoma
Oregon
Pennsylvania
Rhode Island
South Carolina
South Dakota
Tennessee
Texas
Utah
Vermont
Virginia
Washington
West Virginia
Wisconsin
Wyoming

B
Kansas
Kentucky
Louisiana
Maine
Maryland
Massachusetts
Michigan
Minnesota
Mississippi
Missouri
Montana
Nebraska
Nevada
New Hampshire
New Jersey
New Mexico
West Virginia
Wisconsin
Wyoming

C
Delaware
Florida
Georgia
Hawaii
Idaho
Illinois
Indiana
Iowa
Mississippi
Missouri
Montana
Nebraska
Nevada
New Hampshire
New Jersey
New Mexico
South Carolina
South Dakota
Tennessee
Texas
Utah
Vermont
Virginia
Washington

D
Arkansas
California
Colorado
Connecticut
Idaho
Illinois
Indiana
Iowa
Maryland
Massachusetts
Michigan
Minnesota
Nevada
New Hampshire
New Jersey
New Mexico
Oklahoma
Oregon
Pennsylvania
Rhode Island
Utah
Vermont
Virginia
Washington

E
Alaska
Arizona
Colorado
Connecticut
Georgia
Hawaii
Indiana
Iowa
Louisiana
Maine
Michigan
Minnesota
Montana
Nebraska
New Jersey
New Mexico
North Dakota
Ohio
Pennsylvania
Rhode Island
Tennessee
Texas
Virginia
Washington
Wyoming

F
Alabama
Arizona
California
Connecticut
Florida
Hawaii
Illinois
Iowa
Kentucky
Maine
Massachusetts
Minnesota
Missouri
Nebraska
New Hampshire
New Mexico
North Carolina
Ohio
Oregon
Rhode Island
South Dakota
Texas
Vermont
Washington
Wisconsin

Fifty-State Decoder

1. Alabama
2. Alaska
3. Arizona
4. Arkansas
5. California
6. Colorado
7. Connecticut
8. Delaware
9. Florida
10. Georgia
11. Hawaii
12. Idaho
13. Illinois
14. Indiana
15. Iowa
16. Kansas
17. Kentucky
18. Louisiana
19. Maine
20. Maryland
21. Massachusetts
22. Michigan
23. Minnesota
24. Mississippi
25. Missouri
26. Montana
27. Nebraska
28. Nevada
29. New Hampshire
30. New Jersey
31. New Mexico
32. New York
33. North Carolina
34. North Dakota
35. Ohio
36. Oklahoma
37. Oregon
38. Pennsylvania
39. Rhode Island
40. South Carolina
41. South Dakota
42. Tennessee
43. Texas
44. Utah
45. Vermont
46. Virginia
47. Washington
48. West Virginia
49. Wisconsin
50. Wyoming

What a Tree!

SKILLS: Problem Solving
                Time
                Binary System

What a tree! It was at the very end of winter, the last winter day. Spring was ready to begin. All the trees on the lawn were bare. The single tree closest to my house looked barren and desolate. And then it happened. On the very first day of spring, as if by magic, a leaf appeared on one of the cold branches. The leaf was beautiful, well-formed and green. One could not help but notice the leaf because of the sharp contrast of this existing beauty with that of a seemingly motionless and uninteresting tree. And these were the events of the first spring day.

last day of winter

first day of spring

On the second spring day . . . more magic. On another branch of the same tree, another leaf—this one equally as beautiful as the first one. On the third spring day . . . astonishment. The tree had 4 pretty leaves. From then on it was 8 leaves on the fifth day, 16 leaves on the sixth day, and 32 leaves on the seventh day. What a miracle. The rate of growth continued throughout the spring. Following this growth pattern, can you discover how many leaves were on the tree on the tenth day, the sixteenth day, and the twenty-first day? What a fabulous tree!

On the last day of spring, how many leaves were on the tree?

second day of spring

Guess What?

SKILLS:
Estimation
Interpret Data
Number Recognition
Computational Skill—Primary Facts
Problem-Solving Skills

Study the numeral page for exactly one minute. You will be looking at the single-digit numerals 1 through 9. Color the numerals red, white and blue as indicated. Some of the numerals are repeated many times. Study the page carefully and then after the one-minute period, turn the numeral page on its blank side and refer to figure 1.

	Question	Guess	Answer	Difference
1.				
2.				
3.				
4.				
5.				
6.				
7.				

figure 1

Figure 1 is to determine how well you are able to use your powers of observation. This activity can be used by one student. It can also be used by an entire class. (Have the students copy figure 1 on a sheet of paper.) The seven questions in figure 1 refer to the numeral page. After the teacher reads each question, the student is allowed time to record his guess adjacent to the question number. After all seven questions are read and time given for the student to record guesses, the teacher will read the correct answer to each question. This time the student should show the correct answer in the column adjacent to the guess.

The difference column is the difference between your guess and the actual answer. If your guess was 7 and the actual answer is 5, then a difference of 2 is to be recorded in the difference column. If your guess was 7 and the actual answer is 9, then the difference is still 2. The object of the activity is to have the lowest possible score in the difference column total.

Now that you or your class has spent one minute studying the numeral page, be ready to record your guesses for the following questions:

1. How many single-digit numerals are on the page?
2. The numeral 3 is shown more often. How many 3's are on the page?
3. The numeral 1 is shown the fewest times. How many did you see?
4. What is the sum of the red numerals?
5. What is the sum of the blue numerals?
6. What is the sum of the white numerals?
7. What is the sum of the odd numerals?

Total the score in the difference column. The lowest score in the class is the winner.

What is the sum total of the red numerals?

Hmmm...

1. 41 numerals
2. ten 3's
3. one 1
4. red = 55
5. blue = 58
6. white = 64
7. odd = 93

A to Z Math Words

SKILLS: Gather and Interpret Data
           Graphs and Charts
           Problem-Solving Skills
           Development of Math Vocabulary
           Development of Math Research Skills
           Integrate Math with Language Arts

Mathematics is a great deal more than just the writing and recording of symbols and numbers. Mathematics is also the understanding and involvement of a large number of words. This activity has listed over three hundred such words in alphabetical order. Without looking at the list on the following pages, can you write your own list of math words and then compare your findings with the published list? An interesting way to approach this problem might be to choose a different letter each day and devote ten or fifteen minutes on trying to arrive at a matching number of words that begin with that particular initial letter. In the alphabet listed below, the number that is written next to each letter indicates the number of math words included for that particular letter. The range for these findings is from 1 word for the initial letters J and Z to 39 words that begin with the initial letter C.

A-18	H-5	O-12	V-5
B-11	I-14	P-32	W-7
C-39	J-1	Q-6	X-2
D-28	K-3	R-21	Y-2
E-14	L-11	S-21	Z-1
F-10	M-22	T-15	
G-10	N-7	U-8	

Another idea might be to display your discovery in an interesting bar graph and compare your findings with those listed in the book.

40

A

absolute
abundant
accurate
add
addend
adjacent
after
age
algorithm
angle
answer
area
arithmetic
array
associativity
attribute
average
axis

B

base
before
between
billion
binary
binomial
bisect
blank
bottom
bunch
bushel

C

calculator
calculus
calendar
capacity
cardinal
categorize
cent
century
chart
chord

circle
circular
circumference
classification
closed
column
combination
common
commutative
compare
complete
composite
computation
computer
concave
concept
cone
congruent
consecutive
converse
convex
coordinate
corner
correspondence
couple
cube
cup
currency
cylinder

D

data
day
decade
decimal
decrease
definition
degree
depth
design
diameter
diamond
dice
different

digit
dime
dimension
direction
discover
distance
disjoint
division
distributive
dollar
domino
dot
double
dozen
drill

E

east
empty
equal
equidistant
equivalent
estimate
even
exact
example
exceed
exclude
expanded notation
explanation
exponent

F

factor
feet
few
Fibonacci
flow chart
foot
forecast
form
fraction
function

G
gain
gallon
greater than
geometry
gram
graph
grid
gross
group
guess

H
half
height
hexagon
hour
hundred

I
identity
improper
inch
include
incorrect
increase
infinity
information
integer
interest
intersection
interval
invert
isosceles

J
join

K
kilo
kilogram
kilometer

L
least
left
length
less than
line
linear
liquid
location
loop
loss
lowest

M
many
map
mathematics
matrix
maze
mean
measure
median
metric
middle
million
minuend
minus
minute
missing addend
mode
money
month
most
multiplicand
multiplicator
multiply

N
negative
nickel
nil
north
number

numeral
numeration

O
obtuse
odd
one to one
open
operation
opposite
order
ordinal
organize
ounce
oval
over

P
palindrome
parallel
parallelogram
partial
pattern
peck
penny
pentagon
percentage
perfect
pi
piece
pint
place value
plane
point
polygon
position
positive
pound
powers
predict
prime
principle
print

probability
problem
product
program
projective
proper
pyramid

Q
quadrant
quart
quarter
quarterly
question
quotient

R
radius
rank
rate
ratio
rational
ray
record
rectangle
reduce
reference
reflective
regroup
relationship
remainder
repeating
response
rhombus
right
round
round off
row

S
same
sample
second
set
scale
shape
short
side
skill

slope
solution
solve
south
square
statistic
structure
substitute
subtract
sum
symmetry
system

T
table
tally
tens
term
tessellate
thousand
time
ton
top
total
trend
trigonometry
triple
twice
twin

U
under
understand
unequal
uneven
union
unique
unit
unknown

V
value
variable
vector
vertical
volume

W
week
west
wide
width
whole
whole number
why

X
x
x axis

Y
y
y axis

Z
zero

Color Mathematics

SKILLS: Computational Skills
Basic Primary Facts
Interpret Data
Exponents
Binary System
Place Value

Color Mathematics was created and designed to give teachers a method by which they might reach and maintain a high level of pupil excitement and involvement. The base two concept is central to the color math idea. The relationship between the colors and the numerals 1, 2, 4, 8, and 16 (which are the powers of two), is illustrated below.

red	blue	green	yellow	white
16	8	4	2	1

With the assignment of each color to a specific value, we can now determine the color point value of anyone in the class. A blue sweater with green stripes would have a point value of 12, because blue = 8 and green = 4. In another example, blue pants with red pockets and yellow stitching has a point value of 26 (red = 16, blue = 8 and yellow = 2) 16 + 8 + 2 = 26.

The easiest way of determining the point value of a classmate or even yourself is to set up a color line similar to the one shown in figure 1 and then place an X in the appropriate box if you are wearing any of these particular colors.

red	blue	green	yellow	white
16	8	4	2	1

figure 1

Suppose you wanted to find your own point value on any given day. The first question to be asked is "Am I wearing red?" If the answer is yes, place an X in the box below *red*. Continue asking questions regarding the remaining four colors. After each positive response mark an X in the special box. Place no mark in the box where the color response is negative.

Suppose your friend was wearing a blue shirt, white pants and a red belt, what would his color value be? Again, create a color line and place an X in the appropriate boxes.

red	blue	green	yellow	white
X	X			X
16	8	4	2	1

figure 2

In this instance red, blue and white = 25   (16 + 8 + 1 = 25).

There are many follow-up activities for Color Mathematics. One might be to have each child find the point value of his own color scheme on any given day and then order them from a point value from high to low. This can be done by making comparisons with other class members. Imagine the expression on a youngster's face when the teacher asks, "If at all possible, could you please come to school tomorrow dressed in 19 color value points?" Then ask, "What colors will you be wearing?" This scene is something to behold.

Another follow-up idea is to find pictures in magazines and then determine the point value according to the color line. An area in the classroom set aside with magazines would be ideal. Today might be a 10-point picture search. Ask the children to find all the pictures they can with a 10-point total and then place them in the 10-point folder.

Color Mathematics develops and maintains high motivational levels for teachers and students. The children become aware of the environment and its possible association with mathematics. Color Mathematics is also a means for providing open-minded explorations and discoveries.

Scoreboard

SKILLS: Computational Skill Drill
                  Renaming Numbers or Sums
                  Gather and Interpret Data

When playing professional football, your favorite team can score in any of the following ways.

        TD—touchdown = 6 points
        PAT—point after = 1 point (This
                touchdown   score can only
                                  be gotten after a
                                  TD has been scored.)
        S—safety= 2 points
        FG—field goal= 3 points

Other than a team not scoring at all, list the number of ways in which a team could score 6 points.

        TD = 6 points
        3 safeties = 6 points
        2 field goals = 6 points

Complete the following boxes:

7 points	10 points
12 points	13 points

Suppose you watched the game between the Green Bay Packers and the Chicago Bears. Suppose the score was: Chicago   31
                                     Green Bay 30

Try to record all of the ways in which each team might have scored their points.

*Chicago   31   **Green Bay 30**

Make up some of your own game scores and pass them on to classmates. Ask them to record all of the scoring possibilities for your game.

*Chicago's 31 points could have been scored:

5 | TD's | and 1 | PAT |

  (5 x 6)   +   1   =   31

_____

or

2 | TD's | and 2 | PAT | and 5 | FG | and 1 | S |

 (2 x 6)   +   2   +   (5 x 3)   +   2
  12   +   2   +   15   +   2   =   31

47

Gunfight at the O.K. Corral

SKILLS: Computational Skills
            Basic Primary Skills
            Missing Addends
            Listening Skills

From a regular deck of playing cards, this activity requires all cards from ace (1) through 10 for a total of forty cards. Two players come to the front of the room and stand back-to-back. The teacher selects two cards drawn at random and places one in each player's right hand. Each player holds the card pressed against his forehead with the number side facing out. The player holding the card is not to see his card.

With the card at the forehead and both players standing back-to-back, the teacher will command the players to do the following:

1. Each player must take three steps.
2. On command **turn**, players turn and face each other each looking at his opponent's card.
3. The teacher is now ready to call the **sum**!

The objective is to take the information given by the teacher, look at the opponent's card, and determine the numeral on his own card. The first player to correctly do so is declared the winner.

Suppose you, the player, turned on command and heard the teacher call a **sum** of 14 and at the same time you are able to see that your opponent's card is ⁵┐₉ . You should think of the open sentence in your mind.

5 plus how much more do I need to make 14? or

$$5 + \boxed{} = 14$$

The only true solution to the problem is 9 (your opponent's card). In the meantime, your opponent is doing something very similar. He is saying, "9 + $\boxed{}$ = 14." Looking at your card, your opponent can see 9 and heard the **sum** 14.

The player with the correct answer is declared the winner and is now able to challenge other class members. This same procedure is excellent for other basic skill operations such as multiplication.

Swami

SKILLS: Computational Skill Facts Less Than 10
Missing Addend or Open Sentence
Development of Listening Skills

Swami allows for the teaching of the missing addend concept as well as building positive self-esteem in students. Choose someone from the class and explain the activity to him without other class members hearing the explanation.

Select a student to be the Swami. The Swami will be able to determine a number written on the chalkboard without looking at the board. The Swami's back will be to the board and a classmate will write a number less than 10. Upon seeing the number, the teacher will call out a series of five or six numbers. The first number sounded must complement the number on the board because together, both numbers must add up to 10.

Example:

Written on the chalkboard is the number 3. The first number spoken by the teacher must be 7. The following numbers mean nothing when solving the problem: 7, 8, 6, 2, 4, 5.

Instruct the student to listen only to the first number. In his mind, the student must say (as in this instance), "7 plus how much more do I need to have a sum of 10?" The remaining numbers in the series are put there to buy the time that will allow for solving the problem. Again, if you want the student to answer with 6, your first number in the series must be a 4.

Example:

"Michael, is the number on the chalkboard a 4, 6, 3, 8, 9, or 1, or perhaps none of these?"

Mental Number Guess

SKILLS:　　Computational Skill Drill
　　　　　　Exponents
　　　　　　Place Value

Have someone select a number that is smaller than 31. This number is to be kept secret from you. Explain to this person that you will ask questions that he is to respond with a proper yes or no. Instruct the person that eventually he will be down to the number 1, and at this point the correct response is "Stop, we are now at 1." Suppose the number selected and unknown to you is 20. Follow this play:

	YOU	ONE WHO SELECTED THE NUMBER	
a.	"Is your number odd?"	"No"	(20)
b.	"Take half of this number (20). Is it odd?" $(20 \div 2 = 10)$	"No"	(10)
c.	"Take half of this number (10). Is it odd?" $(10 \div 2 = 5)$	"Yes"	(5)
d.	"Subtract 1 from your new number $(5 - 1 = 4)$; now take half of your new number $(4 \div 2 = 2)$. Is it odd?"	"No"	(2)
e.	"Take half of this number (2). Is it odd?" $(2 \div 2 = 1)$	"Yes, and stop. We are at 1."	(1)

In order, these are the responses from the person who selected the number:

a. No
b. No
c. Yes
d. No
e. Yes

Set up the chart to look like this:

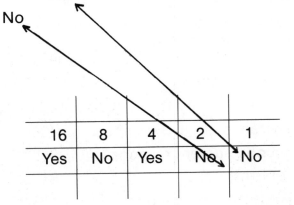

16	8	4	2	1
Yes	No	Yes	No	No

If you add the numbers above **Yes**, your total will be 20.

Wow, How D'ja Do That?

SKILLS: Addition with Regrouping
           Problem-Solving Skills
           Missing Addend

Ask a student to select a three-digit number.

For example, 426.

Let them know that you have the power to correctly predict the **answer**. In this particular instance, the **answer** will be 2,424.

426

_____
2,424

Follow this format:

a. The student's original number 426   (Immediately write
b. Ask the student for another three-   the sum as 2,424.)
    digit number, perhaps   357
c. Your response must be   642
d. Ask for another three-digit number
    perhaps   238
e. Your response must be   761

Now have the students find the sum of all five numerals. Before anything else is written, remember that the answer 2,424 had been predicted.

Big Question: WHY?

SOLUTION: To any three-digit number you add 2,000 -2, or 1,000 -1 two times.

_____ Student's original number   426
_____ Second student response   357   (To reach 999, you must add 642.)
_____ Your response   642
_____ Third student response   238   (To reach 999, you must add 761.)
                                   761
                                  _____
                                  2,424

52

7, 11 and 13

SKILLS: Multiplication/Division Facts
                 Prime Factors

Select a three-digit number . . . 426.
Repeat the digits in the same order and this time create a six-digit number . . . 426426.
Record this number and divide it by 7.

$$\begin{array}{r} 60918 \\ 7\overline{)426426} \end{array}$$

Record the answer, 60918 and divide it by 11.

$$\begin{array}{r} 5538 \\ 11\overline{)60918} \end{array}$$

Finally, take this number 5538 and divide it by 13.

$$\begin{array}{r} 426 \\ 13\overline{)5538} \end{array}$$

Check your final answer and compare it to your original selection. Try this activity again with a new three-digit number. Don't forget to repeat the digits in the same order. The activity requires a six-digit number. Divide this number first by 7, divide the new answer by 11, and divide the next answer by 13. Was your final answer something you expected?

Multiply the factors 7 x 11 x 13. Use this product to multiply any three-digit number. This is also a great calculator activity.

Homebox

SKILLS: Probability
          One-to-One Correspondence
          Computational Skills Drill for Basic Facts

MATERIALS: A gameboard, 2 dice (numbers 1 through 6), 4 movers

A. This game is for two to four players. (You can have as many as three players on a team.)

B. Play begins with the bottom number 1 on the gameboard and proceeds in order until you reach the top number 5. At this point you go into the HOMEBOX.

C. In turn you toss two dice. With the top numerals on each die you may add, subtract, multiply or divide.

D. Play begins for each player or team by first tossing a 1. If a 1 cannot be made with the numbers on the dice, then the dice are to be given to the next player or team.

E. You must start play with a 1. In trying to reach the top of the ladder after making a 1, you must then try for a 2, 3, 4, 6, and 5 in this order.

F. If you make your number, you immediately take another turn.

G. The winner is the first player or team to arrive at the 5.

H. This rule is most important. If you toss a *6 and 6, you are to leave the game.*

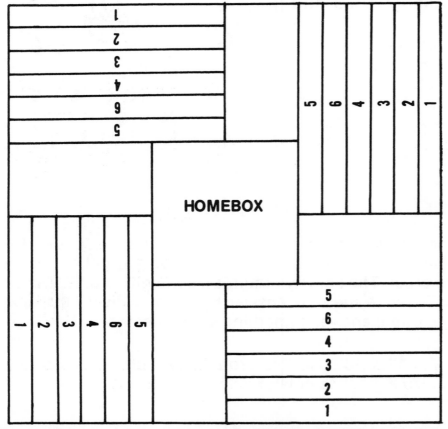

Gameboard measurements in inches:

Board 22″ by 22″
Homebox 9″ by 9″
Blank rectangles 4″ by 6.5″
Numbers 6.5″ by 11.5″

Numbers are written in 1″ spaces.

Snowflakes

SKILLS: Gather and Interpret Skills
           Basic Facts Skill Drill

On each of the three cards is a representation of snowflakes. Some of the flakes are white, some are black and others are striped.

card A   **card B**   **card C**

When given the values for  ,  , and  , can you then determine the value for each of the three cards?

Example:

Suppose we say that **white** = 4, **black** = 3, and **striped** = 2. Can you find the value for card A, card B and card C?

Looking at card A you will see 1 **white** snowflake, 1 **black** snowflake and 2 **striped** snowflakes.

white = 4,
the card has 1 **white** therefore 1 x 4 = 4

black = 3,
the card has 1 **black** therefore 1 x 3 = 3

striped = 2,
the card has 2 **striped** therefore 2 x 2 = _4_
           The total point value for card A = 11.

This time refer to card C.

white = 4,
the card has 2 **whites** therefore 2 x 4 = 8

black = 3,
the card has 1 **black** therefore 1 x 3 = 3

striped = 2,
the card has 5 **striped** therefore 5 x 2 = _10_
           The total point value for card C = 21.

card A

card B

card C

Given the following values, can you determine the point values for cards A, B, and C?

1. If **white** = 10, **black** = 5, **striped** = 4, what are the point values for cards A, B, and C?

2. If **white** = 9, **black** = 10, **striped** = 15, what are the point values for cards A, B, and C?

3. If **white** = 6, **black** = 7, **striped** = 8, what are the point values for cards A, B, and C?

4. If **white** = 1, **black** = ½, **striped** = ¼, what are the point values for cards A, B, and C?

5. If **white** = 1.5, **black** = 1.3, **striped** = 1.1, what are the point values for cards A, B, and C?

At this time you might want to give the point values for the three colors of the snowflakes and then see if your students can determine the point values for cards A, B, and C?

Meaningful Relationships

SKILLS: Fractions
                Relationships
                Area
                Measurement
                Multiplication Facts

This activity stresses the relationship that one part of a figure has on the entire figure. The following problem-solving approach is to determine the area or point value of the overall design. Figure 1 is composed of three different sized parts. Each part has a definite relationship to the other.

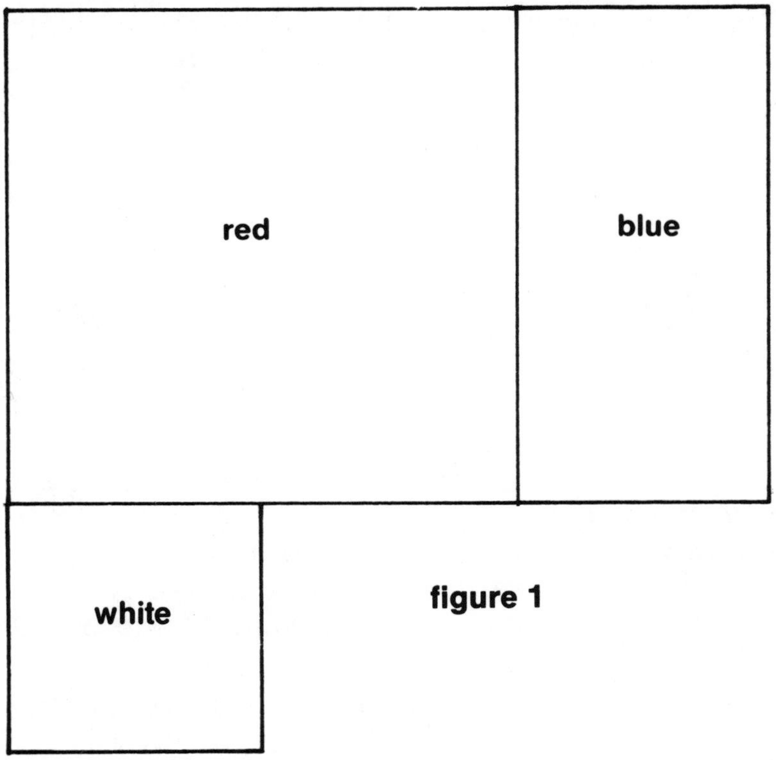

Blue is ½ of red.
Red is two times the size of blue.
White is ¼ of red.
Red is four times the size of white.
White is ½ of blue.
Blue is two times the size of white.

figure 1

It is not difficult to understand these relationships, but it is most important that you do.

If red is two times the size of blue, and if blue = 9, red = 18; 2 x blue = red or 2 x 9 = 18.

The same is true if blue is equal to 5, red = 10; 2 x blue = red or 2 x 5 = 10.

blue = 11, red = 22
blue = 4, red = 8
blue = .3, red = .6

The reverse is also true. If red = 10, blue = 5
red = 16, blue = 8
red = 9, blue = 4.5

The relationship between red and white is important. Referring to figure 1, you can see that red is four times the size of white, and that white is one-fourth the size of red.

Now listen carefully...

If red = 16, white = ¼ of red
white = ¼ x red
white = ¼ x 16 = 4

red = 12, white = ¼ of red
white = ¼ x red
white = ¼ x 12 = 3
or
4 x white = red

By stressing the relationships that one part has with another, we can see that 4 whites = 1 red
2 whites = 1 blue

There is an easier way to arrive at the area or point value of figure 1, and that is to concentrate on the smaller part of the figure. (The smallest part is the white section.) Learn about white's relationship to the overall figure. Decide how many of these small white parts will fit into the red part and the blue part. Now ask, "What is the relationship of white to the overall figure?"

In figure 1, red = 4 whites, blue = 2 whites and the figure has 1 white, therefore the total is 7 whites.

All that is needed now is the value for the white. If it is given that
red = 12, white = ¼ of red or ¼ x 12 = 3
We now have the value for white, and since there
are spaces in figure 1 for 7 whites, then 7 x
3 = 21 which is the point value for the figure.

Refer to the same figure and change the point value for red. If red = 16, figure 1 has a point value of _____?

Can you find the point value for figure 1 if red = 36? 40? 10?

Can you find the point value for figure 1 if blue = 10?

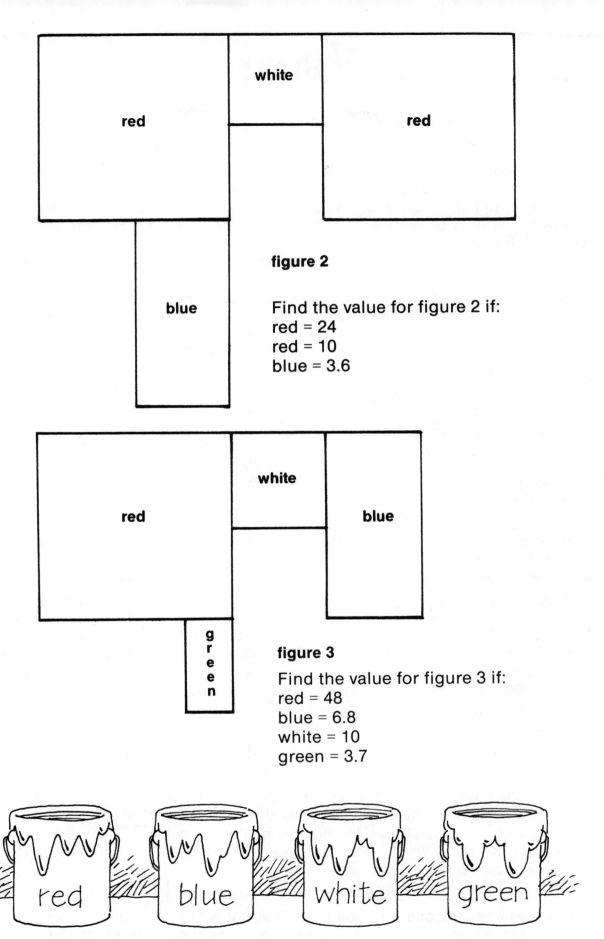

figure 2

Find the value for figure 2 if:
red = 24
red = 10
blue = 3.6

figure 3

Find the value for figure 3 if:
red = 48
blue = 6.8
white = 10
green = 3.7

Panic

SKILLS: Basic Math Facts Drill
             Equations

This game consists of 45 playing cards, 15 orange cards containing answers, 15 yellow cards with the same answers as the orange cards, and 15 white cards on which are written the questions. The game is designed for two players and a neutral third party or for two teams with up to five players on each team and one neutral person. Before play begins, the orange team spreads its answer cards faceup on their side of the playing area. The yellow team does the same with their cards. The neutral person places the white question cards facedown, in a neat pile, in the middle of both playing areas. When the first question card is turned faceup by the neutral party, it is now up to both teams to locate their card containing the correct answer and be the first to elevate it. Calling out answers will not affect the scoring. The correct answer card must be raised from the playing area and it must be read first.

What is the longest river in America? Hmmm...

What is the tallest mountain in America? Hmmm...

Example:

Orange Team

Yellow Team

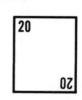

Suppose the next question card shown by the neutral party contains the math equation

The neutral party says nothing but turns the question card over so that all of the players can see the equation card at the same time. In this instance, the first team raising the  card

will be awarded one point. The neutral party will then remove the 20 card from both teams. Play continues until all of the equation cards are shown.

This activity will allow players an opportunity to record some of the excitement created during the game. This happens when the game is down to the last answer card. Suppose the final card for each team is showing [16 / 91] ; we know the answer on the question card is 16.

We do not know the equation. The neutral party would ask all of the players to record on a separate sheet of paper all of the equations that they can think of that have an answer of 16. Team members should be given three minutes to accomplish this. At the conclusion of the allotted time period, all of the written answers should be checked. Any player writing the equation that matches the still unseen equation card will score 10 points for his team. In the meantime, the teacher now has a large collection of equations with an end result of 16.

HURRAY ! OUR TEAM WON!

YEA!

Startime

SKILLS: Computational Skill Drill for Basic Facts
Addition, Subtraction, Multiplication and
Division

On white poster board construct two stars. Each star should be the same in size, color and numbers. An ideal size might be in the range of 14" by 14". The center of the star is to be cut out.

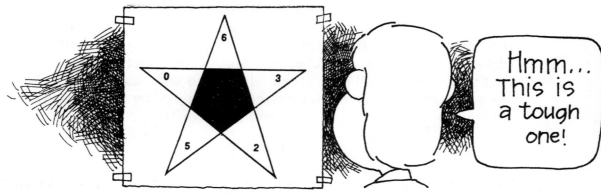

The activity calls for the stars being taped to the chalk-board. Instruct the class that you will write a number and a math operation (+, ÷, ×, —) in the cutout part of each star. The student assigned to that star should then try to solve all five points on the star according to the operation chosen by you, the teacher.

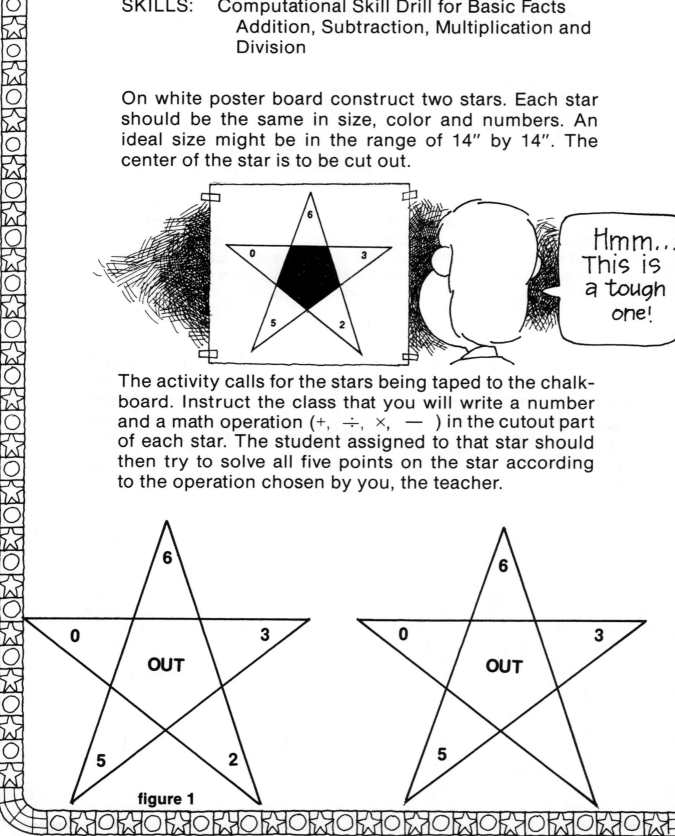

figure 1

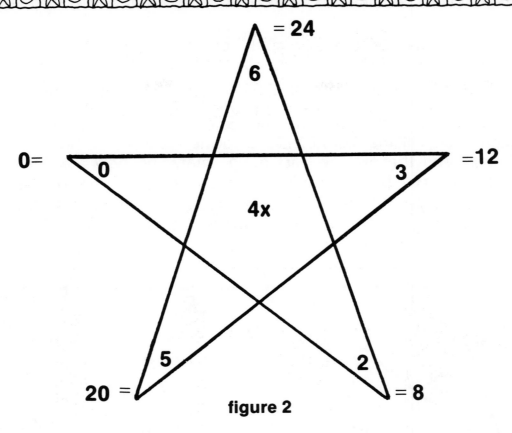

figure 2

At this point, tell the class that you will divide them into two teams (A and B). Choose one player for each team. The two players are to go to the chalkboard and stand in front of their respective stars with their backs to the chalkboard. While each player is facing the class, the teacher will write a number and an operation in the cutout part of each star, a different number for each star.

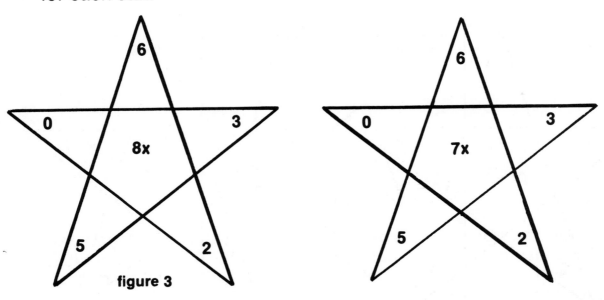

figure 3

On the command of the teacher, the players will look at the number and operation in each star. The player should use this information to arrive at the answers for all five points. When finished, the teacher will check all answers. All correct answers are worth one point. Once this is completed and the point value for each player is determined, all the teacher has to do is erase the inside part of the star and the outside part of the star, and now ask for new players. With each new round, the teacher can record new problems.

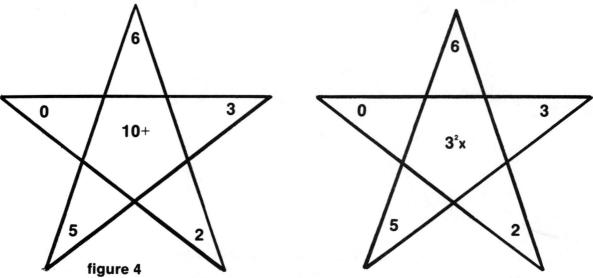

figure 4

The same activity can be extended to language arts. Turn the star on the other side and the five points might show:

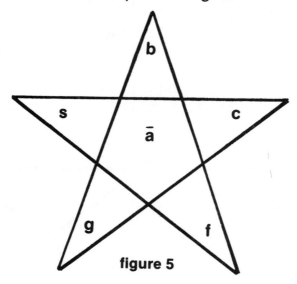

figure 5

With the star on this side, you might want to review long vowel sounds. In the cutout part you might write ā. Tell the players they are to write four or five-letter words that contain the point letter and the vowel sound.

Checkerboard Square

SKILLS: Problem Solving
Patterning
Figurate Numbers (Square Numbers)

Question: How many squares are on an 8" x 8" checkerboard?

It is not difficult to determine the exact number of squares on the checkerboard if you correctly use your power of observation. When asked the above question, most people respond with 64 squares. There are always those who will see one more square for a total of 65 squares, the sixty-fifth square being the one very large square. At closer study, the checkerboard will reveal that there are not only 64 squares that measure 1" x 1" and one large square that measures 8" x 8", but you can also find squares that measure 2" x 2", 3" x 3", 4" x 4" and so on.

The next step to solving the pattern is to organize this information and begin to search for patterns.

It has been decided that the checkerboard consists of 64 squares measuring 1" x 1". Examine the following order:

> 1" x 1"
> 2" x 2"
> 3" x 3" . . . since the largest square is 8" x 8",
> then it would stand to reason that there would also
> be squares that measure . . .

4" x 4"
5" x 5"
6" x 6"
7" x 7"
8" x 8"

If you add this additional information, the solution may seem reachable.

In the checkerboard there are

64 squares that measure 1" x 1".
49 squares that measure 2" x 2".
36 squares that measure 3" x 3".
__ squares that measure 4" x 4".
__ squares that measure 5" x 5".
__ squares that measure 6" x 6".
__ squares that measure 7" x 7".
1 square that measures 8" x 8".

Upon a closer look at the number pattern generated by the known number of squares (64, 49, 36 . . .), you can see the pattern for square numbers in descending order. Consider the next square number in this pattern. Fill in the missing number of squares. Now total the sum of the eight square numbers, and you will have the answer to the original question: How many squares are on an 8" x 8" checkerboard?

Finger Multiplication

SKILL: Computational Skill Facts for Multiplication

Multiplication facts can be taught by using your fingers. Consider the following:

Each finger carries with it the value as shown in figure 1. If the problem is to multiply 9 x 9, align your fingers according to the example shown in figure 2.

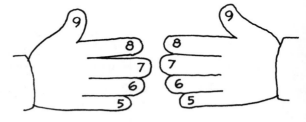

figure 1

When multiplying 9 x 9, the two thumbs must touch. All fingers shown below the connection represent a point value of 10. Figure 2 shows eight fingers below the connection. This represents *eight 10's*. Once this partial product is determined, the next step is the *pull apart. Before you pull apart, tuck the eight fingers in tight, and then pull apart.*

figure 2

What you have now is one thumb free on the left hand and one thumb free on the right hand, and so you may now multiply 1 x 1 = 1.

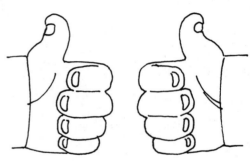

figure 3

This partial product in addition to the previous product of *eight 10's* gives a final product of 81. Another example: 8 x 7.

Align both hands so that the 8 finger connects with the 7 finger as in figure 4.

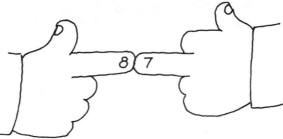

figure 4

Determine how many fingers are below the connection. In figure 4 you will see five fingers (equal to five 10's). Once this is determined, *pull apart.*

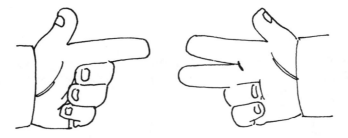

This time you have three fingers free on the left hand. Multiply this by the two fingers free on the right hand and you should have a partial product of 6. The partial product 6 plus the partial product of five 10's or 50 gives a final product of 56 or 8 x 7 = 56.

Silent Lesson

SKILL: Patterning with Numbers

For an almost complete change of pace, try the Silent Lesson. The teacher should pretend that he has just lost his voice and this condition will probably last through the entire period. With a piece of chalk in one hand and a board eraser in the other hand, consider the following. The teacher writes on the chalkboard:

Boys and girls, I would appreciate your helping me to get through this period. I lost my voice; however, I can still write. I'll put a pattern on the board. Please don't call out the answer. Raise your hand and I will point to you. Again, please help complete this pattern.

```
3
6
9
.
.
```

With this approach in mind, the teacher can review any desired language arts or number pattern. This idea of a silent lesson is a unique change that you might want to try at least once a month.

Another example:

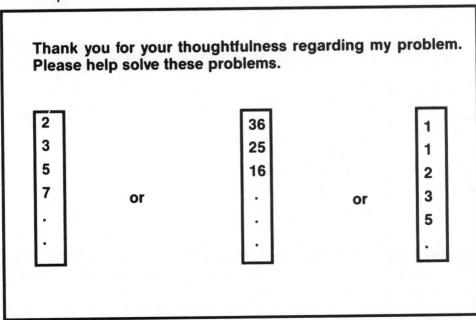

Thank you for your thoughtfulness regarding my problem. Please help solve these problems.

```
2            36              1
3            25              1
5            16              2
7            .               3
.            .               5
.            .               .
```

or   or

Prime Numbers   Square Numbers   Fibonacci Numbers
(add the last two numbers
3 + 5 = 8)

Pattern Search

SKILLS: Patterning
           Problem-Solving Skills

Pattern Search will help in the development of necessary problem-solving skills. Each grid below contains its own unique patterning sequence. Each sequence follows its own unique path.

On examination, figure 1 is a grid that measures 5 x 6. It contains the numerals 1, 2 and 3. The idea is to uncover the intended numeral sequence. Once this is established, follow the path of the sequence through the grid to its conclusion. In figure 1 the numeral sequence is 1, 1, 2, 2, 3. This sequence can be followed by looking at the upper left cell in the grid and then proceeding downward. (You should see the sequence begin with 1, 1, 1, 2, 2.) At this point, change the direction to a horizontal right and the final numeral in the sequence can be found (3). By following the upward vertical path of the arrow, you will see that the numeral sequence repeats itself for a complete grid total of five times.

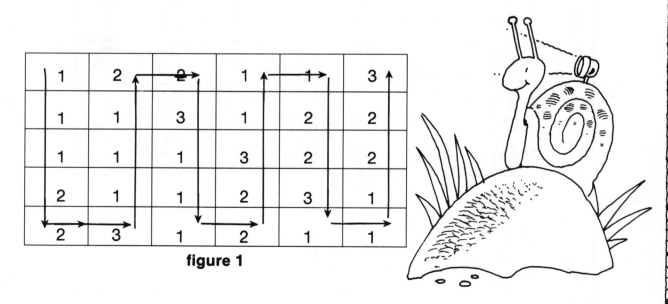

figure 1

Try the pattern search for figure 2. This search begins with the numeral 4 and has a total of six numerals in its pattern. Once again, try to find the path of its repeated sequence.

9	2	1	6	2
6	1	2	9	4
2	4	9	2	1
2	9	4	2	6
1	6	2	4	9
4	2	6	1	2

figure 2

Figure 3 contains the name of a famous sports personality. The letters used in this grid are those found in this person's name.

E	R	P	O	E	T	S	T
R	P	S	T	S	R	O	P
T	O	S	O	S	E	S	T
E	S	O	R	E	T	E	P

figure 3

R	O	B	E
E	B	O	R
R	T	R	T
T	R	T	R
R	O	R	O
E	B	E	B

Try creating your own pattern search using the letters in your first name.

Pascal's Triangle

SKILLS: Computational Skill Drill for Basic Facts
Addition, Subtraction, Multiplication and Division
Number Patterning
Figurate Numbers (Square Numbers 1, 4, 9, 16, Triangular Numbers 1, 3, 6, 10)
Probability
Gathering and Interpreting Data

A	B	C	D	E	F	G
1						
1	1					
1	2	1				
1	3	3	1			
1	4	6	4	1		
1	5	10	10	5	1	
1	6	15	20	15	6	1

figure 1

This unique number pattern (Pascal's Triangle) has been exciting students and teachers for many, many years. There are also many different ways of arriving at the numbers in the pattern. Examine figure 1 and try to uncover some possible pattern discoveries.

Example:

In column A you will see a **vertical line of constant ones.**
Column B has **counting numbers in a vertical line.**

There are diagonal patterns. There is a **diagonal line of constant ones** as well as a **diagonal line of counting** numbers.

There are horizontal patterns:
The sum of the numbers in the first row is 1.
The sum of the numbers in the second row is 2.
The sum of the numbers in the third row is 4.
Can you predict the sum of the numbers in the next six rows?

Look for cross column patterns.

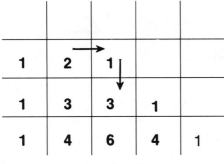

$$2 + 1 = 3$$

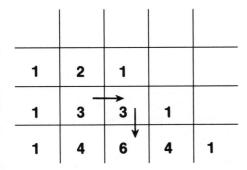

$$3 + 3 = 6$$

With this cross column pattern in mind, can you complete this segment?

1	4	6	4	1			
1	5	10	?	5	1		
1	6	15	?	?	?	1	
1	?	?	?	?	?	7	1

One more interesting pattern and then you are on your own. Refer to figure 1. Choose any number in column B (perhaps 3); look at its neighbor in column C (3) and the number immediately below its neighbor (6). If you square the 3, the answer can be found in column C, because $3^2 = 9$

B   C
3   3
       6

$$3^2 = 3$$
$$+6$$
$$9$$

again . . .

Good luck in your pattern search.

B   C
4   6
     10

$$4^2 = 6$$
$$+10$$
$$16$$

50 Beans

SKILLS: Place Value
             Computational Skills

MATERIALS: Twenty tongue depressors
             (get these from the
               school nurse)
             One large bag of jelly beans
             One tube of white glue
               (Elmer's)
             One set of dice (numerals
               1 through 6)

Ready each tongue depressor by squirting ten drops of glue at equal intervals onto each stick. Just before the glue begins to solidify, set a jelly bean in the drops. Give it a few minutes and the jelly bean will stick to the white glue. You now have what is known as a **ten-bean stick.**

figure A   A ten-bean stick
               with a value of
               10.

figure B   Unit beans.
               Each bean has a
               value of 1.

Players will see that:
       three, ten-bean sticks = 30
       seven, ten-bean sticks = 70
       also that:
       two, ten-bean sticks and six unit beans = 26
       five, ten-bean sticks and four unit beans = 54

Once this is established, explain to the players (and that could be anywhere from four players to four teams with two or three players on each team) that the winning team is the first team to reach 50 points or 5, ten-bean sticks. In turn each team will toss the dice on to a flat surface. The sum of the dice indicates the number of unit beans the player will receive. The teacher or leader should dispense the correct number of unit beans.

Remind the players that they are striving for a total of 50 beans. Also inform the players that as soon as a player has 10 unit beans, the player is to trade with the leader. Trades are 10 unit beans for one, ten-bean stick. This practice should continue until one team reaches 50 points.

Follow this play after one round of tossing dice.

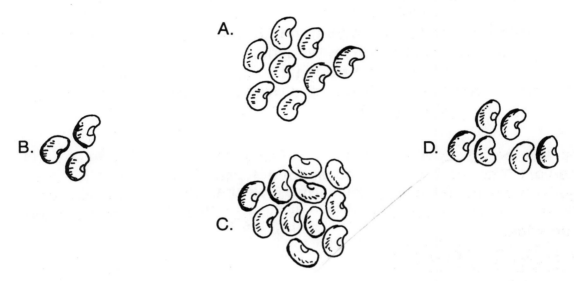

A has 8 points, B has 3 points, C has 11 points, and D has 6 points. Since C has 10 or more unit beans, C is to trade 10 unit beans to the leader in exchange for 1, ten-bean stick. The play will now look like this:

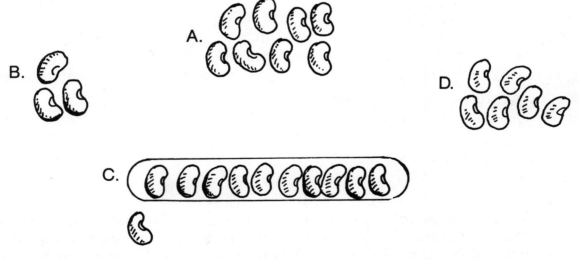

Again in turn each team will take its turn at tossing the dice and trying to accumulate unit beans. The goal . . . 50 points or five, ten-bean sticks.

Hatch It

SKILLS: Multiplication Facts
           Division Facts
           Arrays

For another approach to understanding the development in multiplication and division, the crosshatch method might be a most relevant idea. Starting with multiplication, have the students construct vertical and horizontal lines (freehand). Suppose you wanted to write the problem 4 x 3.

The first factor 4 requires that you draw four vertical lines.

The second factor 3 requires that you draw three horizontal lines to be constructed over the drawn four vertical lines.

At all points where the lines intersect, make a dot.

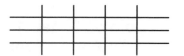

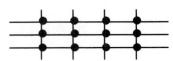

If you count the number of dots, you will see that 4 x 3 or 4 times 3 is equal to 12.

The next example shows the problem and answer to 3 x 6. Remember that the first factor (3) is for vertical lines and the second factor (6) is for horizontal lines. Don't forget to make a dot at every intersecting point.

Set up solutions for the following problems:

2 x 7   7 x 2   0 x 8   3 x 9   5 x 0

For a new look at division, examine the multiplication problem 3 x 7—three vertical lines, seven horizontal lines.

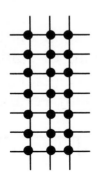

Now write the division problem

5 $\overline{)21}$

Looking at the 3 x 7 grid you will see 21 dots. To divide, you arrange the 21 dots into groups with 5 dots in each group.

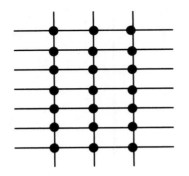

You can now see four groups with five dots in each group. We know that 4 x 5 = 20, and if you look carefully you can see the one remaining dot.

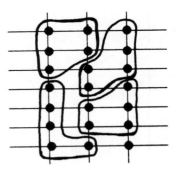

Try the following:

3 $\overline{)21}$ 4 $\overline{)21}$ 6 $\overline{)21}$ 7 $\overline{)21}$

Creative April

SKILL: Basic Facts

The following grid is a representation of the month of April. The dates and days are not written in the usual calendar fashion that we are accustomed to seeing. In lieu of these missing dates, you will find creative expressions that refer to the dates. For example: 3 = little pigs, 13 = baker's dozen, 21 = blackjack. Make the month of April more creative by completing the remaining boxes.

The completion of this month can be in the area of math. For example: 7 = 10 - 3 or 15 = 5 x 3, etc.

		$1000-110$ two two	little pigs			
						baker's dozen
		sweet				
black-jack			4!			

Mister E. Cent Tens

SKILLS: Problem Solving
           Ordinals
           Computational Skill Facts

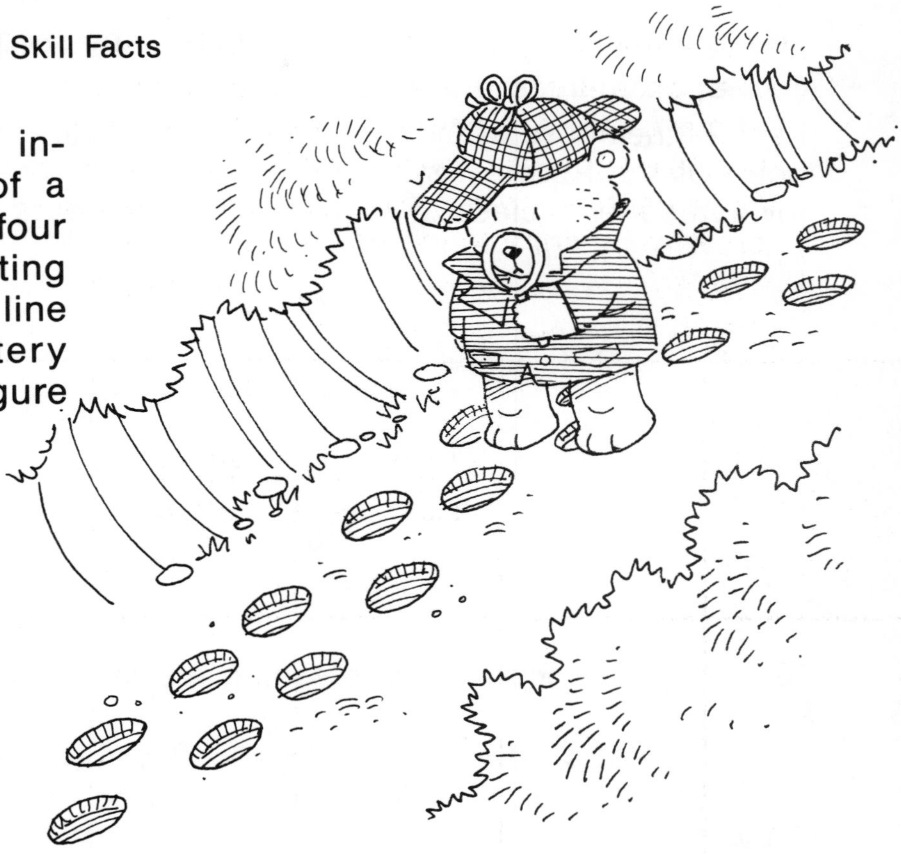

The following activity involves the decoding of a
sentence that contains four
words. Space for writing
letters is held by short line
segments. The mystery
sentence is shown in figure
1.

— — — — — —

— — — — —

— — — — — —

— — — —

figure 1

Participants should be told that the line segments represent words that are made
up of consonants and vowels. Each consonant has a point value of 1 and each
vowel a point value of 5. If you total the value of the entire sentence, you will
find the point value to be 45. The line segments are arranged in ordinal position,
first, second, etc. Play begins with someone asking to see all of the letters that
are placed in the second position, perhaps. If this is the request, the teacher is
to disclose all letters in the second position for all four words.

_ h _ _ _ _

_ n _ _ _

_ h _ _ _ _

_ u _ _

figure 2

Once the positions are recorded, the point value disclosed is to be subtracted
from the total sentence value. The sentence in figure 1 has a point value
of 45. The point value of the given clues is 8.

Subtract 8 from 45 and the highest possible point value at this time is 37. After each set of clues is given by the teacher, the players are given five free guesses to correctly decode the unsolved word configurations. Referring to figure 2, examine the second word. It has five letters. Can you think of five-letter words with an **n** in the second position?

Some possibilities: enter, India, under

Each of the above would fit the requirements for the second word; however, none of the above words are to be used in figure 2. At this point, ask for someone in class to request another ordinal position, perhaps third.

_ h a _ _ _

_ n j _ _

_ h u _ _ _

_ u n _

figure 3

Don't forget to score. Before seeing the clues in figure 3, the score was 37.

The new letters will cost the players 12 points; therefore 37-12 = 25. The 25 is a possible score if the players can correctly decode the sentence. In the second word the clue **j** should provide help. Someone (with each new set of clues, five more guesses) might guess the second word to be *enjoy.*

This is the correct word and the letters **e, o** and **y** should be encircled. (figure 4)

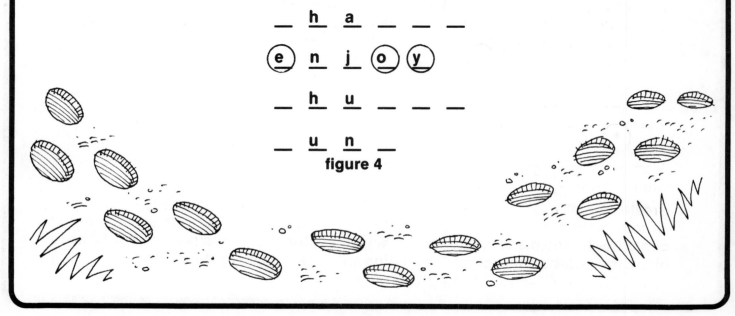

_ h a _ _ _

(e) n j (o) (y)

_ h u _ _ _

_ u n _

figure 4

The encircled letters total 11 points. This is the minimum score. Once five new guesses are used, ask someone to select a new position—perhaps the fourth position.

```
_   h   a   r   _   _

ⓔ  n   j   ⓞ  ⓨ

_   h   u   n   _   _

_   u   n   a
```

figure 5

Again, don't forget to score. The possible score was 25, but new clues will cost 7 points; therefore 25 - 7 = 18 for correctly decoding the sentence without additional clues. As for one of the five new guesses, a player might want to solve the fourth word and guess *tuna*. If so, circle the **t**. It would be an earned point. If the first and third words are still not solved, give the fifth position to the players.

```
_   h   a   r   k   _

ⓔ  n   j   ⓞ  ⓨ

_   h   u   n   k   _

ⓣ  u   n   a
```

figure 6

Remember to subtact 2 points for the two consonants. The possible total score is now at 18. At this point a player might guess that the third word is *chunky*, in which case the teacher would circle the **c** and **y**. Someone might guess the first word as being *sharks*. This time circle the first **s** and the last **s**. The decoded sentence would read:

```
ⓢ  h   a   r   k   ⓢ

ⓔ  n   j   ⓞ  ⓨ

ⓒ  h   u   n   k   ⓨ

ⓣ  u   n   a
```

With consonants given a point value of 1 and vowels a point value of 5, the encircled letters in the sentence have a total point value of 16.

Create your own four-word sentence. Once you have written the sentence, determine its total point value. Your arrangement of the sentence should be similar to that of figure 1. Begin the activity by disclosing all second position letters in each of the four words and see if the participants can discover your message.

Prime-Mates

SKILLS: Prime and Composite Numbers
Multiplication and Division Facts
Prime Factorization
Fractions
Reducing Fractions

A 1	B 2	C 3	B B 4	5	6
7	8	9	10	11	C BB 12
13	14	15	16	17	18
19	20	21	22	23	24
25	26	27	28	29	30

figure 1

Figure 1 is a grid that represents boxes numbered 1 through 30. During this activity, 1 should be referred to as **A**, 2 = **B**, 3 = **C**, 4 = **BB**, and 12 = **CBB.** These should be considered the clue boxes.

82

The following dialogue will help to complete figure 1:

"We have 30 boxes and 5 of them contain letters. Your task is to solve the remaining boxes using a letter or a combination of letters. In working toward the solution, use a separate sheet of paper. Now choose a box and try to solve its letter equivalence. Whichever numbered box is selected, let me know what you have created; and if it is correct, I will give you the OK to write your response in its proper box in the grid. For example, suppose you thought that 9 = BBBC. I would think that you used the operation of addition. You probably thought that 2 + 2 + 2 + 3 = 9. My response to you would be that you did not create the letter symbol for 9, but you did create the letter symbol for 24. (Actually the chart calls for multiplication 2 x 2 x 2 x 3 = 24)." Rather than indicate to the students that the only acceptable operation is multiplication, continue seeking responses for the remaining boxes.

Perhaps someone trying to solve box 5 might offer, "5 = BC." Your response might be something like, "You're saying that 2 + 3 = 5. That's great except 2 WITH 3 IS EQUAL TO 6. Therefore BC = 6." Have the student record BC in the 6 box.

The more attempts made at trying to solve this puzzle, the easier it will be to find its solution. At some point instruct the class that the only acceptable operation is multiplication. The factors for 18 are 3 x 3 x 2. When you create the letter substitution for 18, the answer is CCB. The factors for 5 are 5 and 1. Whenever you have a box that contains only two letters, as is the case with 5, the letter conversion is the next available letter of the alphabet. In this situation, 5 is equal to the letter D. Again stress that there is to be no addition or subtraction. Division is a possibility that will appear later in this activity.

The Solution

A ₁	B ₂	C ₃	BB ₄	D ₅	BC ₆
E ₇	BBB ₈	CC ₉	BD ₁₀	F ₁₁	BCB ₁₂
G ₁₃	BE ₁₄	CD ₁₅	BB BB ₁₆	H ₁₇	CCB ₁₈
I ₁₉	BBD ₂₀	CE ₂₁	BF ₂₂	J ₂₃	BBBC ₂₄
DD ₂₅	BG ₂₆	CCC ₂₇	BBE ₂₈	K ₂₉	DBC ₃₀

To complete these follow-up activities you may wish to refer to the solution.

If:
        B = 2   B   B
        D = 10   D   D
                        E = 70

What would be the product of:

B	C	D
D	C	B
E	B	C
D	B	E
<u>A</u>	<u>A</u>	<u>A</u>

Which of the problems below has the smallest product? The largest product?

E	C	F	D
D	B	B	D
B	D	D	B
B	C	B	B
B	B	B	E
<u>A</u>	<u>A</u>	<u>A</u>	<u>A</u>

84

The solution chart allows for still another approach to teaching and understanding some of the properties of multiplication.

Commutativity:	CB = BC
	3 x 2 = 2 x 3
Identity:	DA = D
	5 x 1 = 5
Associativity:	(BC) D =B (CD)
	(2 x 3) 5 = 2 (3 x 5)

Prime and Composite Numbers

We should say that the solution chart is completed only when all of the boxes include the letter A.

A 1	BA 2	CA 3	BBA 4	DA 5	BCA 6
EA 7	BB BA 8	CCA 9	BDA 10	FA 11	BB CA 12

The prime numbers are represented in those boxes that contain exactly two letters, the letter itself and A (the number itself and 1). Examples of this idea are shown in boxes 2, 3, 5, 7 and 11. The remaining boxes (excluding 1) are called composite numbers. It may be interesting to note that 2 is the only even prime number.

An awareness of the solution chart affords the opportunity to deal with another approach to fractions, in particular, the concept of reducing fractions.

Again, the following example may help.

$\frac{B}{C}$, once the letter to numeral conversion is made, reads $\frac{2}{3}$.

Try solving these:

$$\frac{D}{BE} \qquad \frac{CC}{BD} \qquad \frac{B}{CC}$$

$$\frac{E}{BD} \qquad \frac{BC}{E} \qquad \frac{BB}{CC}$$

The fraction $\frac{12}{15}$ is not reduced to its lowest term. Once you convert this fraction to letters, an alternative solution is possible.

$$\frac{12}{15} = \frac{BBC}{DC}$$

The solution involves searching for common letters that appear in both the numerator and denominator. In the sample problem above, the common letter is C. The process calls for a cancellation of the common letter and a renaming of the remainder the fraction:

$$\frac{12}{15} = \frac{BB\cancel{C}}{D\cancel{C}} = \frac{BB}{D} = \frac{4}{5}$$

Reduce each of the following to its lowest term:

$$\frac{10}{15} \qquad \frac{18}{20} \qquad \frac{6}{15}$$

The idea of being able to divide was mentioned earlier in this activity. Using the letter chart with this math concept is equally interesting. Consider the problem whose product is 9800.

B
D
E
D
B
E
B
A

If the following question were asked, how would you arrive at an answer?
   "With a dividend of 9800, is this dividend divisible by 56 and if so, will there be no remainder?"

Excuse me, sir... With a dividend of 9800, is this dividend divisible by 56 and if so, will there be no remainder?

Come again?

The answer to the first question is yes. 9800 is divisible by 56. The answer to the second question is yes. There will be no remainder. The process as to how this solution is accomplished is most interesting when you consider the prime factorization of 9800.

If you consider the first question, "Is 9800 divisible by 56?" simply cross out all of the factors (all the prime factors) of 56 or BBBE.

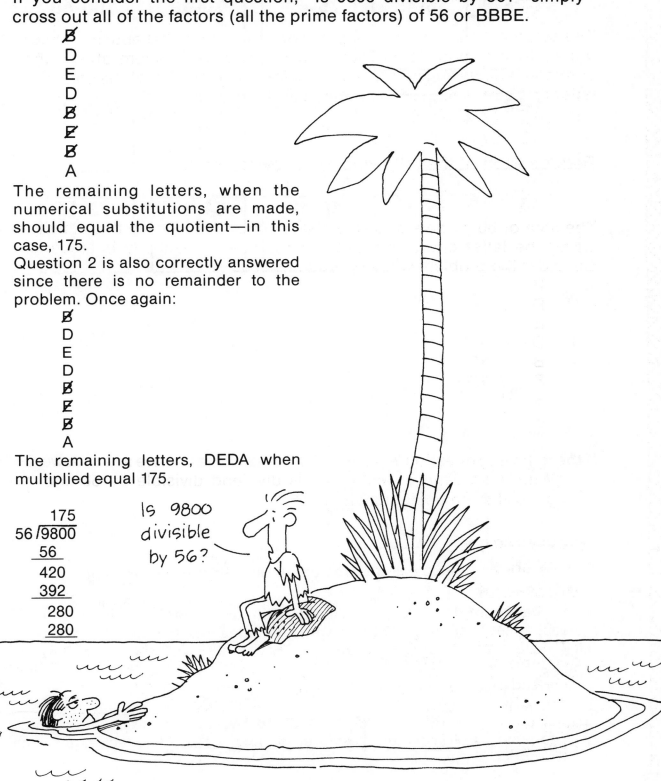

~~B~~
D
E
D
~~B~~
~~E~~
~~B~~
A

The remaining letters, when the numerical substitutions are made, should equal the quotient—in this case, 175.

Question 2 is also correctly answered since there is no remainder to the problem. Once again:

~~B~~
D
E
D
~~B~~
~~E~~
~~B~~
A

The remaining letters, DEDA when multiplied equal 175.

```
        175
  56 /9800
       56
      ----
      420
      392
      ----
      280
      280
```

Is 9800 divisible by 56?

Prime Time Players

SKILL: Prime and Composite Numbers
MATERIALS: Product Cards (3" x 5")

54-28	**36-45**	**75-42**	**70-49**	**100-40**
24-63	**56-35**	**60-25**	**30-36**	**125-20**
27-90	**48-80**	**50-10**	**64-98**	**72-15**

Prime Factor Cards (3" x 5")

2	16 cards
3	10 cards
5	7 cards
7	4 cards
wild	2 cards

(This card can be any prime number—2, 3, 5, or 7.)

Question Cards (3" x 5")

front

3 prime factors

back

How many ounces in 3 lbs.?

The fronts of the Question Cards can have values anywhere from one to three Prime Factor Cards.

The backs of the Question Cards will ask questions involving measurements such as feet in 3 yards, minutes in a half hour, cookies in 2 dozen, days in 3 weeks, etc.

Rules:

1. The game is for two to four players.

2. Each player is dealt a Product Card and given a piece of paper on which to write. On this paper, the player is to write the prime factors for each product.   Example:

      100   40
      5 x 5 x 2 x 2   2 x 2 x 2 x 5

3. In turn, the teacher will ask each player a question found on the back of the Question Card deck.

4. If the response is correct, the player is entitled to the number of Prime Factor Cards indicated on the front of the Question Card.

5. In the example on the work sheet, $100 = 5 \times 5 \times 2 \times 2$ and $40 = 2 \times 2 \times 2 \times 5$.

6. By answering the Question Card correctly, perhaps the player is entitled to 3 Prime Factor Cards. Perhaps the cards were 5, 2 and 7. The 5 and the 2 are needed to create the product 100 or the product 40.

7. Perhaps on the player's next turn, he answered the next question correctly and this time is entitled to 3 Prime Factor Cards. Suppose these were 2, 2 and 3.

8. Combined with the other Prime Factor Cards, this player would have enough prime factors to make the product 40.
$5 \times 2 \times 2 \times 2 = 40$

9. On the work sheet, the player would circle the 40. This player earned 40 points and is entitled to another Product Card.

10. Play continues until someone reaches three products. At this point, all of the players should then total their completed products and the player with the largest point total is the winner.

11. A player can win the game with only one completed product if that product is greater than the sums of the product of another player.

Let's play Prime-Mates!

I Have, Who Has . . . ?

SKILL: Metric Awareness

Here is a great idea for a drill that will eventually lead to an increased understanding of the metric system. Distribute the activity cards among the class members. Let them know that the sixteen activity cards are similar to the links in a chain. With all of the chain links intact, you are able to start a chain at any point and complete its entire course once you have returned to the initial starting point. In this chain activity the person chosen to begin the chain will read the card aloud and then wait for the next participant to read the only card that would correctly follow the progression. After each participant reads his card, he should pause and wait for the next player to acknowledge his place in the chain by reading the appropriate card. Play continues until all of the cards are read and the initial student is ready to read his card for a second time.

The activity cards below are not written in any particular order. However, as the chain progresses, you will eventually return to the starting point (assuming that no links are missing).

The following is a description of the sixteen activity cards.

Card No. 1

Front

I have decimeter.

Back

Who has one thousand grams?

I have 100° Celsius...

Who has one-tenth of a meter?

Card No.	Front	Back
2	I have 100° Celsius.	Who has one-tenth of a meter?
3	I have milligram.	Who has the metric unit for 100 meters?
4	I have kilogram.	Who has one-one hundredth of a meter?
5	I have dekameter.	Who has one-thousandth of a liter?
6	I have kilometer.	Who has the normal human body temperature in Celsius?
7	I have liter.	Who has the metric temperature on a very cold winter's day?
8	I have hectometer.	Who has the metric unit of length you would use to measure the distance from one city to another?
9	I have meter.	Who has the metric unit of measurement for temperature?
10	I have 37°C.	Who has the metric unit that is one-ten millionth of the distance from the North Pole to the Equator?
11	I have centimeter.	Who has one-tenth of a centimeter?
12	I have -20°C.	Who has ten times a meter?
13	I have millimeter.	Who has one-one thousandth of a gram?
14	I have gram.	Who has the metric unit of volume that is a little more than a quart?
15	I have millimeter.	Who has the metric boiling point of water?
16	I have Celsius.	Who has the metric unit of weight to describe a paper clip?

I have centimeter...   Who has one-tenth of a centimeter?

I Have, Who Has . . . ?

SKILLS: Fractions   Equivalent Fractions
          Addition and Subtraction of Fractions

The idea of the chain as a teaching aid will be used again in this activity for fractions and equivalent fractions.

Distribute the cards among the class members. Select someone to begin the chain and read the card aloud and then wait for the next participant to read the only card that would correctly follow the progression. After each participant reads his card, remember to pause and wait for the next player to acknowledge his place in the chain by reading the appropriate card.

The following is a description of the sixteen activity cards.

Card No.	Front	Back
1	3½	I have 3½. Who has its double?
2	½	I have ½. Who has ¼ more?
3	3⅜	I have 3⅜. Who has 2 less?
4	2	I have 2. Who has ⅞ more?
5	4¾	I have 4¾. Who has ¾ less?
6	1¼	I have 1¼. Who has 3½ more?
7	⅜	I have ⅜. Who has ⅛ more?
8	6⅞	I have 6⅞. Who has 6½ less?
9	3	I have 3. Who has 3 more?
10	1⅜	I have 1⅜. Who has ⅝ more?
11	4	I have 4. Who has ⅝, less?
12	6	I have 6. Who has 2½ less?
13	7	I have 7. Who has ⅛ less?
14	⅛	I have ⅛. Who has 1⅛ more?
15	2⅞	I have 2⅞. Who has ⅛ more?
16	¾	I have ¾. Who has ⅝ less?